INTRODUCTION TO ASTROPHYSICS

The Stars

(*Introduction à l'astrophysique: les étoiles*)

by
JEAN DUFAY
Director of the Observatory of Lyon
and Haute Provence

Translated from the French by
OWEN GINGERICH
Harvard College Observatory

Dover Publications, Inc., New York

TRANSLATOR'S PREFACE

The past decade has witnessed a remarkable surge in the publication of astronomical works. Within a few years, the number of basic textbooks was doubled, and the number of popular accounts increased by an even larger factor. Nor has the production of technical and specialized works flagged.

Nevertheless, a significant gap exists in the publication in English of *intermediate* level books—works appealing to the physicist, engineer or chemist, who, lacking an astronomical background, nonetheless finds the standard texts too pedestrian for his own scientific training, or appealing to the advanced amateur as well as the astronomy undergraduate, who, being already acquainted with the introductory texts, wish something not quite so detailed as the advanced astronomical monographs.

When Jean Dufay's *Introduction à l'astrophysique: les étoiles* was sent to me for review by *Sky and Telescope* magazine, I recognized it as an excellent guide to observational astrophysics, of the sort quite scarce in English. Instead of reviewing the book, I have, with the much appreciated support of the editorial staff at Dover Publications, translated it!

This translation, with minor exceptions, follows the original work quite closely. In several cases I have added an additional phrase of supplementary information or explanation. The metric dimensions of American and English telescopes have been converted back to inches. Some of the more technical material, placed in smaller type in the French edition, has not been so distinguished here.

Prof. Dufay has in general avoided the more speculative aspects of present-day astrophysics. Only in his penultimate sentence does he make a statement that should now be modified. In the light of the most recent studies of the nuclei of certain spiral galaxies, I have taken the liberty of adding "generally" to his sentence.

Cambridge, Massachusetts
April, 1963

OWEN GINGERICH

FOREWORD

Two volumes in the *Collection Armand Colin* have already treated important aspects of astronomy. *L'Astronomie Générale* by Luc Picart contains the fundamental ideas of positional astronomy, applied especially to the solar system. *L'Astronomie Stellaire* by Jean Delhaye describes the knowledge acquired more recently about the distances and movements of stars, the kinematics and dynamics of the galactic system and of distant galaxies.

Initially astrophysics was to be the subject of a third volume. But the application of physical methods to the study of celestial bodies that has taken place in the last half century has led to developments so important and so varied that it has become completely impossible to give even an elementary account in so small a number of pages. The work which I present today thus represents only an *introduction* to astrophysics, limited to the study of stars in general.

I have taken it upon myself, first to describe simply, but in a precise manner, the present methods of stellar photometry and spectroscopy (and, in this spirit, I have deliberately ignored the techniques no longer used), then to make known the general results of observations concerning the classification of normal stars and their properties.

These are in fact the basic ideas, indispensable to a more advanced study of the diverse problems of astrophysics. Only in the last chapter do I refer to some theoretical notions in order to seek an interpretation of the empirical classifications and to give a brief summary of the present ideas on the constitution of stellar atmospheres and the probable evolution of stars.

The unstable stars, variables and novae, are laid aside in spite of the great interest they present. They will be studied more profitably along with galactic nebulae and interstellar matter in another volume devoted to the Milky Way and to the galaxies, which will shortly complete this *Introduction à l'Astrophysique*.

I wish to thank MM. Daniel Barbier, Daniel Chalonge, André Couder and André Lallemand, who have read my manuscript and aided me with their advice.

CONTENTS

Contents

CHAPTER I

DEFINITIONS AND SPECIAL CONDITIONS IN ASTRONOMICAL PHOTOMETRY

I. STELLAR BRIGHTNESS, APPARENT MAGNITUDE AND ABSOLUTE MAGNITUDE

1. Stellar brightness and magnitudes

Stellar brightness designates the illumination that is produced on a surface normal to the luminous radiation from some source. In the case of point sources such as stars, this is the only photometric quantity directly accessible to measurement.

Let the brightness of two stars be E_1 and E_2. By definition their *magnitude difference* is the quantity

$$m_1 - m_2 = -2.5 \log (E_1/E_2). \tag{1.1}$$

Thus to a *difference* of magnitude there corresponds a certain *ratio* of stellar brightness. This relation, known as *Pogson's equation*, can also be written

$$\log (E_1/E_2) = -0.4(m_1 - m_2)$$

or

$$\frac{E_1}{E_2} = 2.512^{-(m_1 - m_2)}.$$

When the difference of magnitude of two sources is -1, the ratio of their brightness is 2.512. More generally, a magnitude difference of $-2.5n$ corresponds to a ratio of 10^n to 1. Thus the brightness of a first magnitude star is 100 times greater than that of a star of sixth magnitude ($n = 2$) and 10,000 times greater than that of a star of magnitude 11.0 ($n = 4$).

In order to have a particular magnitude correspond to each stellar brightness, we must arbitrarily fix the magnitude of some star as a standard, to determine the zero point of the scale.

DIFFERENT MAGNITUDE SYSTEMS.—Magnitude differences measured in monochromatic light, for example on a spectrogram at a particular wavelength, have a perfectly well defined sense entirely independent of the receiver used. This is not always the case when measurements are carried out over an extended spectral region. If the energy distribution is not the same in the spectra of the two sources, the spectral sensitivity of the receiver plays a role. Receivers of distinct *selectivities*, such as the eye, a photographic plate or a photoelectric cell, no longer give the same magnitude difference. Only *neutral* or *non-selective* receivers always measure the ratio of luminous energy. This is obviously the case for *thermal* receivers, such as bolometers, radiometers or thermocouples.

To each selective receiver there corresponds a particular magnitude system. In each of these the zero point of the scale is fixed by special convention. Thus the convention with respect to the Harvard visual magnitudes rests on assigning a magnitude of $+6.55$ to the star λ UMi,[1] observable throughout the year at nearly the same altitude because of its proximity to the north celestial pole.[2]

Before photometric measures, observers in antiquity had arranged the stars visible to the naked eye into six classes of brilliance, of which the 6th corresponded to the faintest stars. Later it was recognized that, due to a characteristic of the eye, these primitive magnitudes were approximately proportional to the logarithms of the stellar brightnesses. Thus to define precisely the difference in magnitude a relation was required of the form

$$m_1 - m_2 = k \log (E_1/E_2)$$

where k would be a negative constant, since the brightness diminishes as the number expressing the magnitude increases. The value $k = -2.5$ has been chosen to approximate as nearly as possible the same differences in magnitude between the stars as in the ancient classification. The convention in setting the zero point also tends to bring the magnitudes themselves into agreement with those attributed to various stars by the ancients.

The comparison of the brightness of a star whose visual magnitude has been determined, with the brightness produced at a known distance by a source calibrated in *candelas*, permits the linking of the

[1] See Table XI at the end of this volume for the abbreviations designating the principal constellations.

[2] Polaris (α UMi), taken originally as a reference star, had to be abandoned since its brightness, measured visually, varies by about 10% with a 3.96-day period.

system of visual magnitudes to the ordinary photometric units (one candela equals about 0.98 "old" candle). The magnitude corresponding to a brightness of 1 lux (produced by 1 cd at a distance of 1 m) would be -14.2. Thus we can evaluate, in luxes, the brightness of a star of visual magnitude m_v by the relation

$$\log E = -0.4(m_v + 14.2). \tag{1.2}$$

The brightness produced by stars of magnitudes 1.0 and 6.0 will be 8.3×10^{-7} and 8.3×10^{-9} lux, respectively.

2. Luminosities and absolute magnitudes

When the stellar brightness E of a source and its distance r is known, we can evaluate its luminosity or luminous intensity by the relation

$$I = Er^2, \tag{2.1}$$

which expresses the conservation of luminous flux and which is true only in the absence of all absorption. We thus calculate the luminous intensity of a source in watts, if we know the brightness in watts per cm² that is produced a distance of r cm, or its visual intensity in candelas, if we know the brightness of the source in luxes and its distance in meters [14].[3]

In astrophysics we prefer to compare the intensities of stars in another manner. If the stars were all located at the same distance, their brightnesses would obviously be proportional to their intensities. We can thus take as a measure of their intensities either the brightnesses or the magnitudes that would be observed if all the stars were placed at a fixed distance. It is convenient to choose this unit for the scale of stellar distances. To evaluate the distance of stars we adopt as our unit the *parsec* (abbreviated *pc*), the distance of a star whose annual parallax would be exactly 1″. Between the annual parallax in seconds of arc and the distance in parsecs, we have the relation [4]

$$r = 1/p. \tag{2.2}$$

[3] The numbers between brackets refer to the corresponding entries in the bibliography.

[4] The radius a of the terrestrial orbit (considered as circular) will be seen from the star subtending a variable angle in the course of a year; the maximum value is called the *annual parallax* of the star [8, 26]. In radians this gives $p = a/r$, and in seconds of arc, $p = 206,265 \ a/r$ (since 1 radian $= 206,265″$). By taking as the unit of length $206,265 \ a = 3.086 \times 10^{13}$ km $= 1$ parsec, we obtain the relation (2.2).

In many popular works the distances to stars are expressed in *light-years*. One light-year is the distance traveled by light in 1 year, being about 9.46×10^{12} km. Therefore, 1 pc equals 3.26 light-years.

For convenience we reduce the stellar brightness to the value that would be observed at a fixed distance of 10 *parsecs.* The corresponding magnitude M is called the *absolute magnitude.* In contradistinction, the magnitude m considered up to now takes the name *apparent magnitude.*

Beginning with this definition, we immediately establish the relation that connects the absolute magnitude M with the apparent magnitude m and the distance in parsecs r. In the absence of absorption, the stellar brightness E_r and E_{10} measured at distances r and 10 pc are, according to (2.1), inversely proportional to the squares of the distances,

$$E_r/E_{10} = 100/r^2$$

or

$$\log (E_r/E_{10}) = 2 - 2 \log r$$

and, according to the definition of magnitude difference (1.1),

$$m - M = 5 \log r - 5. \qquad (2.3)$$

This quantity is known as the *distance modulus.*

There are naturally as many systems of absolute magnitudes as systems of apparent magnitudes. For example, we can employ absolute visual magnitudes M_v and photographic magnitudes M_{pg} in conjunction with visual and photographic apparent magnitudes.

When the starlight traverses an absorbing region, the preceding formulas are no longer applicable, since there is no conservation of luminous flux. The apparent magnitude is augmented by the quantity A, which represents the absorption in magnitudes, and we must write

$$m - M = 5 \log r - 5 + A. \qquad (2.4)$$

It is then necessary to know A in order to evaluate the absolute magnitude beginning from the apparent magnitude and the distance.

With a knowledge of a stellar magnitude in lux, we can immediately link absolute visual magnitudes M_v to the ordinary units of luminosity. One candela, at the distance $10 \, \text{pc} = 3.086 \times 10^{17}$ m, produces the brightness

$$E = 1/(3.086 \times 10^{17})^2 = 1.05 \times 10^{-35} \text{ lux}$$

and, according to (1.2), would correspond to the magnitude $M_v = +73.2$. The luminosity of a star of absolute visual magnitude M_v is thus given in cd by

$$\log I = -0.4(M_v - 73.2).$$

Taking the absolute visual magnitude of the sun as $M_v = +4.84$, we find for its luminosity $I = 2.2 \times 10^{27}$ cd. A giant star of absolute magnitude $M_v = 0$ would give $I = 1.9 \times 10^{29}$ cd.

3. Luminance, radiance and apparent diameter

Luminance.—When the apparent diameter of a source is appreciable (sun, moon, planets, nebulae . . .) the stellar brightness is not the only quantity accessible to measurement. We can evaluate in addition the *luminance*.

Let σ be the apparent surface of a source whose intensity is I in the direction of the observer; this is the projection of the surface S on a plane normal to the line of sight. We call the *luminance* of the source in the direction considered its intensity per unit of apparent surface,

$$B = I/\sigma.$$

Upon introducing the luminance into the relation (2.1), valid in the absence of absorption, we obtain

$$E = I/r^2 = B\sigma/r^2 = B\omega, \tag{3.1}$$

since σ/r^2 measures the small solid angle ω under which the source is seen at the distance r.

Luminance can thus be considered as *the stellar brightness produced by a unit solid angle at the source.* This second definition is particularly advantageous in astrophysics, since it is unnecessary to introduce the uncertainties from either the linear dimensions of the source or its distance. It can even be applied to a source whose linear dimensions are indeterminate, such as the celestial sphere.

Just as the magnitude m corresponds to a stellar brightness E, there also corresponds to the luminance B a magnitude m_1 of a unit solid angle. The relation (3.1) is then written

$$m = m_1 - 2.5 \log \omega. \tag{3.2}$$

Radiance.—The radiance or luminous emittance of a source is, by definition, *the flux radiated by a unit surface element of the source in all exterior directions.* No idea of direction is attached to the radiance, which, as in the emission of radiation, plays an analogous role to brightness in its reception, and is expressed in the same units (watt·cm^{-2} in the case of energy measurement, lumen·cm^{-2} or lumen·m^{-2} in the case of visual measurements).

Let us evaluate the radiance of a source as a function of its luminance B, which varies with the angle θ measured with respect to the normal of the surface. Each element of apparent surface $d\sigma = dS \cos \theta$, in a solid angle $d\omega = 2\pi \sin \theta \, d\theta$ taken between the cones of semi-aperture θ and $\theta + d\theta$, radiates the flux

$$B(\theta) \, d\sigma \, d\omega = 2\pi B(\theta) \, dS \sin \theta \cos \theta \, d\theta$$

and radiates in all directions the total flux

$$dW = dS \int_0^{\pi/2} 2\pi B(\theta) \sin \theta \cos \theta \, d\theta.$$

The radiance thus has the expression

$$\mathscr{R} = \frac{dW}{dS} = \int_0^{\pi/2} 2\pi B(\theta) \sin \theta \cos \theta \, d\theta.$$

When the luminance is the same in all directions (we then say that the source radiates according to Lambert's law, and such is the case for a black body), the radiance becomes simply

$$\mathscr{R} = 2\pi B \int_0^{\pi/2} \sin \theta \cos \theta \, d\theta = \pi B.$$

The case of stars.—It is now useful to demonstrate that the brightness produced by a spherical source is proportional to its radiance. We assume that on each point of the sphere of radius R the luminance is the same along the normal and that it is a function of the angle θ according to the same (unknown) law.

Let us take as a surface element the zone bounded on a sphere by the cones with half-angles of θ and $\theta + d\theta$ and apices at O (Fig. 1).

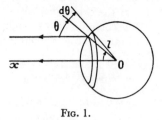

Fig. 1.

In the direction Ox of a distant observer, the apparent surface of the zone is $d\sigma = dS \cos \theta = 2\pi R^2 \sin \theta \cos \theta \, d\theta$ and its luminance is $B(\theta)$. The zone thus produces, at the distance r, the brightness

$$dE = 2\pi \frac{R^2}{r^2} B(\theta) \sin \theta \cos \theta \, d\theta = \frac{\alpha^2}{4} 2\pi B(\theta) \sin \theta \cos \theta \, d\theta,$$

because R/r is the apparent semi-diameter $\alpha/2$ of the sphere.

The total brightness produced by the entire source is therefore

$$E = \frac{\alpha^2}{4} \int_0^{\pi/2} 2\pi B(\theta) \sin \theta \cos \theta \, d\theta = \frac{\alpha^2}{4} \mathscr{R}. \qquad (3.3)$$

This expression will serve to evaluate the color temperature of stars (Chap. VI) and their effective temperature (Chap. VIII).

In what follows we designate by B and $\mathscr{R}$ the luminance and radiance relative to an extended spectral interval, and by b_λ and ρ_λ the monochromatic luminance and radiance, defined by

$$b_\lambda = dB/d\lambda \quad \text{and} \quad \rho_\lambda = d\mathscr{R}/d\lambda,$$

which are expressed in watt$\cdot$cm^{-3} or in erg$\cdot$s$^{-1}\cdot$cm^{-3}.

II. ATMOSPHERIC ABSORPTION

Starlight is seriously modified by its passage through the terrestrial atmosphere, where the radiations of different wavelengths are weakened unequally. The absorption also varies with the zenith distance of the stars and the location of the observer. Even from the same place, for the same zenith distance and wavelength, the absorption sometimes changes in a short interval of time, thus imposing special precautions and care in the methods of measurement.

4. The transmission factor, optical density and the absorption coefficient [14]

A cylindrical beam of monochromatic light traversing normally an absorbing layer with parallel faces has, at the entrance face, a brightness E_0, and at the exit face, a brightness $E_1 < E_0$. The ratio $T = E_1/E_0$ is the *transmission factor* of the layer (<1), whereas the inverse ratio $O = E_0/E_1$ is its *opacity* (>1). It is convenient to introduce the *optical density*, base-10 logarithm of the opacity,

$$D = \log O = -\log T,$$

since many absorbing layers traversed successively, of densities D_1, $D_2, \ldots$, are equivalent to a single layer of density $D = D_1 + D_2 + \ldots$.

In a homogeneous absorbing medium each infinitesimal element of thickness dx, traversed normally, possesses an optical density proportional to dx:

$$dD = a\,dx.$$

The constant a, characteristic of the medium for the radiation considered, is its *absorption coefficient*. This is the optical density per unit length, which has for its dimension inverse length and can be expressed, for example, in cm^{-1}.

The optical density corresponding to a finite element x is the sum of all the densities of the infinitesimal sections and yields $D = ax$. If we replace D by its expression as a function of brightness E at the distance x from the entrance face, and the initial brightness E_0, we can write

$$\log (E/E_0) = -ax \quad \text{or} \quad E = E_0 \times 10^{-ax}.$$

This is the exponential law of absorption, established by Bouguer in the eighteenth century, and which can be cast into the form

$$E = E_0 e^{-kx}$$

where

$$k = a/\log_{10} e = 2.303 \ldots a = a/0.434 \ldots.$$

In most practical applications we use the decimal absorption coefficient a, but the coefficient k is introduced more naturally in theoretical questions.

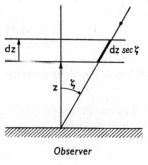

Observer

Fig. 2.

5. Variation of the absorption as a function of the zenith distance: Bouguer's method

By assuming that its properties are uniquely a function of altitude, the atmosphere can be treated, as in the classical theory of refraction, as a series of thin layers, stratified concentrically to the earth, each of which possesses a well-defined absorption coefficient.

If the zenith distance is less than 60–65°, we can neglect both the effect of refraction ($<2'$) and the curvature of the earth. The light rays then traverse rectilinearly a series of plane-parallel layers (Fig. 2). In traversing a layer of thickness dz, characterized by its absorption coefficient a, the trajectory of a light ray coming from a star with a zenith distance ζ has the length $dz \sec \zeta$ and the corresponding optical density is

$$dD = a \, dz \sec \zeta.$$

The total optical density of the atmosphere at the zenith distance ζ is the sum of the elements of optical density of the successive layers

$$D(\zeta) = \sec \zeta \int_{z_0}^{\infty} a \, dz.$$

The integral can be carried out from the ground (altitude z_0) up to infinity, but the absorption coefficient a vanishes at the upper limit of the atmosphere. If $D(0)$ represents the optical density at the zenith for a station, then we can write

$$D(\zeta) = D(0) \sec \zeta.$$

Thus, to evaluate the optical density at a zenith distance ζ less than 65°, it is unnecessary to know the law of the variation of the absorption coefficient a as a function of the altitude. It suffices to know the optical density at the zenith, and the preceding relation furnishes the means to determine it from observation.

Replacing $D(\zeta)$ by $\log(E_0/E)$, we can in effect write

$$\log E = \log E_0 - D(0) \sec \zeta. \tag{5.1}$$

The logarithm of the brightness received at the ground is a linear function of $\sec \zeta$. From this follows Bouguer's method:

Plot the variation in brightness E when a star is rising or setting, using $\sec \zeta$ as abscissa and $\log E$ as ordinate of the graph. The points will fall in the vicinity of a straight line whose slope is $D(0)$ and whose ordinate at the origin is the logarithm of the brightness above the atmosphere, E_0. Instead of the logarithm of the brightness, we can use magnitudes for the ordinate (Fig. 3). The equation of the line becomes

$$m = m_0 + \Delta m_0 \sec \zeta.$$

The slope $\Delta m_0 = -2.5 D(0)$ is the "loss of magnitude at the zenith," and the ordinate at the origin m_0 is the magnitude above the atmosphere.

For the absorption coefficient a to have a definite value, the measures must be made in light that is approximately monochromatic. Applying Bouguer's method to a spectral interval that is too extended would make no sense. The method also presupposes that the configuration of the stratified layers remains stable for the duration of the measurements, which is in general several hours. This condition is not always satisfied, even with a clear sky, so that even in good weather, Bouguer's method sometimes proves inapplicable.

When the zenith distance exceeds 65°, we can neglect neither the curvature of the earth nor the refraction. It is necessary to consider layers limited by concentric spheres, and that the optical density of a thin layer depends on its altitude and thickness. Let us restrict ourselves here to an examination of the case where the absorption is produced throughout all the mass of the atmosphere. The absorption coefficient is then proportional, at each altitude, to the specific mass.

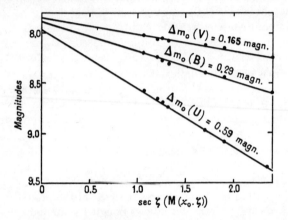

FIG. 3. VARIATIONS OF THE MAGNITUDE OF A STAR IN THE YELLOW (V), BLUE (B) AND ULTRAVIOLET (U), AS A FUNCTION OF THE AIR MASS (photoelectric measurements by J. H. Bigay).

The lines have been shifted vertically by arbitrary amounts; the magnitudes above the atmosphere are: V = 8.77, B = 9.94, U = 10.75 (spectral type K0).

Let δ_z be the density of the gas at altitude z *relative* to gas taken at the standard conditions, and let a_0 be the absorption coefficient at standard conditions. We have

$$a = \delta_z a_0$$

and the optical density at the zenith distance ζ can be written

$$D(\zeta) = a_0 \int_{z_0}^{\infty} \delta_z \, ds,$$

the integral being taken along the curved ray that traverses the atmosphere to the altitude z_0 of the station. Toward the zenith, the optical density is

$$D(0) = a_0 \int_{z_0}^{\infty} \delta_z \, dz.$$

We thus have

$$\frac{D(\zeta)}{D(0)} = \frac{\int_{z_0}^{\infty} \delta_z \, \mathrm{d}s}{\int_{z_0}^{\infty} \delta_z \, \mathrm{d}z} = M(z_0, \zeta).$$

The quantity $M(z_0, \zeta)$ is called the *air mass* relative to the zenith distance ζ and the altitude z_0. We can evaluate the mean of the data received from sounding balloons on the variations of pressure and temperature as a function of altitude (tables by Link). Bouguer's method can thus be applied to zenith distances greater than 65° by using $M(z_0, \zeta)$ as the abscissa in place of sec ζ.

6. Molecular diffusion and atmospheric obscuration

Atmospheric absorption results from the superposition of several phenomena:

1. the *selective* absorption that the gases of the air exercise on certain radiation;

2. the weakening resulting from the diffusion of the light by gaseous molecules;

3. the diffusion (and eventual absorption) by foreign particles retained in the air by suspension (aerosols).

First we shall examine the results obtained apart from the bands of selective absorption. At a high altitude (above 2000 m, for example) the optical density of the atmosphere at the zenith is in general only slightly greater than that which results just from the molecular diffusion of air alone. This molecular diffusion obeys the Rayleigh-Cabannes laws, which have been well verified by experiment. At a station where the atmospheric pressure is p, the optical density at the zenith arising from molecular diffusion in a dry atmosphere can be calculated by the formula

$$D(0) = 4.58 \times 10^{-4} \frac{p}{p_0} \frac{(\mu_0 - 1)^2}{\lambda^4}, \tag{6.1}$$

where λ is the wavelength in microns, μ_0 the index of refraction of the air under normal conditions at wavelength λ, and p_0 the standard atmospheric pressure.

In a first approximation, if we neglect the variation as a function of λ in the index μ_0, the optical density is inversely proportional to λ^4. It is, therefore, 16 times greater for the violet ($\lambda \simeq 0.4\ \mu$) than at the beginning of the infrared ($\lambda \simeq 0.8\ \mu$) and about 256 times greater for $\lambda = 0.2\ \mu$. When the computation includes the increase of the refractive index toward the short wavelengths, the ratio of the optical density at 0.2 μ to that at 0.8 μ actually becomes 360. The molecular diffusion, therefore, would be sufficient to *progressively* extinguish the ultraviolet radiations at the ground. On the other hand, molecular diffusion is practically negligible in the near infrared: the fraction of radiation lost at sea level for a source at the zenith is less than 1% for wavelengths of about 1 μ.

At low altitudes atmospheric obscuration (smog) plays an important role, quite variable from one day to another. Particles whose dimensions are large with respect to the wavelengths diffuse all radiation more or less equally, and produce an essentially neutral absorption, which adds to that arising from molecular diffusion. Those whose dimensions are comparable to the wavelengths diffuse according to very complex laws (§ 50). In all these cases the optical density measured at the zenith is greater—and sometimes very much greater—than the value calculated by the formula (6.1).

7. Selective absorption

We say that molecular diffusion produces only an *apparent* absorption, because the radiation lost for the observer who receives the transmitted light is nevertheless all present in the form of diffused light. The intensity of the diffused light is, like $D(0)$, essentially proportional to λ^{-4}, and the predominance of radiation of short wavelengths explains the blue color of a clear sky.

On the other hand, the selective absorption that certain molecules exert on specific radiation is a *true* absorption, in the sense that the radiation energy which has disappeared is used to dissociate molecules into atoms or to ionize them, or is used to increase their potential energy (electron energy, energy of vibration and rotation). The first case corresponds to continuum absorption in the spectrum, the second to more or less narrow bands that can often be resolved into fine lines.

True atmospheric absorption singularly limits the domain of observable radiation. Only two windows allow the passage of star-light: the first and narrower, from about 0.3 μ to 25 μ, served as the basis for all classical astronomy. The second is found in the domain of Hertzian waves with lengths of several millimeters to a score of meters, and has given birth more recently to radio astronomy. We thus understand the intense interest to astrophysics of observations made with rockets at high altitude or by means of artificial satellites above the atmosphere, which now permit the extension of the study of stellar radiation up to the shortest ultraviolet and to X-rays.

The bands of atmospheric absorption observed in the interval 0.3–25 μ increase in intensity with increasing zenith distance of the star; they do not participate in the Doppler displacement arising in the true solar spectrum from the rotation of the sun. These two characteristics in general allow these so-called telluric lines to be distinguished easily from the absorption bands and lines produced in the solar atmosphere. (The second applies to bands resolved into fine lines, such as those of O_2 and H_2O.)

In the visible region we find relatively weak bands of water vapor (notably at 0.59 μ and 0.65 μ) and the bands of molecular oxygen, diminishing toward the red: band A at 0.760 μ, B at 0.687 μ, and α at 0.627 μ. In the near infrared the bands of H_2O dominate, then those of CO_2. We have also discovered bands in the infrared of molecules rare in the atmosphere: CO, N_2O, CH_4, and the isotopic molecules HDO, H_2O^{17}, H_2O^{18}, $C^{13}O_2^{16}$, $C^{13}O^{16}O^{18}$, $C^{13}O^{16}$, $C^{12}O^{18}$.

However, the molecule that absorbs the most energy (between 0.31 and 0.22 μ) is ozone, O_3, whose abundance is at a maximum around an altitude of 25 km, although very weak in the vicinity of the ground. Reduced to standard conditions of temperature and pressure, the total ozone content of the atmosphere would occupy a layer around the earth with a mean thickness of less than 3 mm. Nevertheless, this is the gas that cuts off the solar and all stellar spectra sharply around 0.3 μ, where the molecular diffusion would have produced only a progressive extinction. The absorption coefficient of ozone, under standard conditions, is therefore enormous in the ultraviolet ($a = 126.5$ cm^{-1} for $\lambda = 0.2553$ μ).

The large ultraviolet band is continued up to about 0.34 μ by bands of increasing narrowness and weakness. (Below 0.20 μ the absorption is produced by O_2 molecules.) The ozone also possesses a very weak absorption region from green to red ($a \leqslant 0.06$ cm^{-1}) and infrared bands, the only ones that are resolved into lines, between 3 and 10 μ, the strongest being at 9.6 μ.

8. Practical conclusion

The magnitude difference of two stars, $m - m'$, measured at the earth, depends on the loss of light introduced by atmospheric absorption in the direction of the two stars. If the measurements are made in approximately monochromatic light and if the atmosphere is sufficiently homogeneous and stable so that we can consider the absorption to be independent of azimuth and constant between the two observations, the loss in magnitude is proportional to the air mass. We can then deduce from the measurements the magnitude difference above the atmosphere, $m_0 - m_0'$, which is the only well defined sense. For zenith distances of less than 65°, we can write

$$m_0 - m_0' = m - m' - \Delta m_0(\sec \zeta - \sec \zeta').$$

It is necessary to determine, by Bouguer's method, the magnitude loss at the zenith, Δm_0, at the time of the observations. Even at one place, especially at low altitudes, the absorption varies too much from one night to another to adopt a mean magnitude loss.

We can avoid these rigid conditions only if the two stars are observed simultaneously or nearly so at about the same zenith distances and, as far as possible, in similar azimuths. The correction applied to the magnitude difference $m - m'$ to reduce it to above the atmosphere can then be so small that it is sufficient to know only roughly the value of Δm_0.

Suppose, for example, that we compare at sea level two stars that are 43° and 45° from the zenith, respectively, and that the measurements are made at the wavelength 0.44 μ. If only molecular diffusion intervenes, we have, according to formula (6.1), $\Delta m_0 = 0.262$ magnitude, and the correction $\Delta m_0 (\sec \zeta - \sec \zeta')$ would be 0.012 magnitude. If the atmospheric obscuration has the effect of doubling Δm_0 (which would be enormous), the correction would become 0.025 magnitude. Thus it is adequate, for 0.01 magnitude accuracy, to know Δm_0 within 10%.

III. ATMOSPHERIC DISTURBANCES

9. Scintillation and the appearance of an image

The image of a brilliant star, examined under rather high magnification at the focus of a refractor at least 20 cm wide, often appears agitated. Around the central image, the diffraction rings are pierced by luminous condensations; sometimes they are broken. Sometimes they disappear completely, while the central image becomes enlarged and diffuse.

Remove the eyepiece from the telescope and, placing your eye at the focus, view the objective. When the images are perfectly calm, it is uniformly bright. But most of the time rapidly moving shadows traverse it, in general taking the form of undulating bands vaguely parallel and equidistant. These are closer and more contrasty when the images are more agitated. Sometimes two systems of striae cross and interlace.

These observations demonstrate that at the objective, the luminous waves coming from a star are not rigorously planar; they present undulations vaguely analogous to the waves of the sea. Therefore the brightness varies from point to point at the objective: it is greater where the rays converge, fainter where they diverge and so the shadows appear there. Seen with the naked eye, the star twinkles or scintillates; its brightness diminishes each time a shadow passes over the pupil, whose diameter is not more than 8 mm. The star does not scintillate if we observe it with a telescope whose diameter is large with respect to the width of the shadows, but the image is agitated because the rays are departing from different points of the objective with rapidly varying phase differences.

The existence of inhomogeneities in the atmosphere accounts for these phenomena. Small local variations in the index of refraction in a moving layer produce irregularities in the surface of the wave at the earth, which are more noticeable when the disturbed layer is higher. These can be caused by inequalities in the temperature of the air, and are associated with high altitude winds, whose directions are in agreement with those of the striae.

10. Turbulence and accidental refractions [9]

The normal to the surface of the original wave and the normal to a surface element of the perturbed wave form at each instant a rapidly varying angle θ. On a photographic plate in rapid motion a star image will trace a sinuous path that permits a measurement at very small intervals of the deviation perpendicular to the motion of the plate. The frequency curve obtained is practically that of a random phenomenon (Gaussian distribution), and this *turbulence* can be characterized by its *dispersion* (or root mean square error) $t = \sqrt{\overline{\theta^2}}$ (A. Couder).

We can also evaluate the turbulence by observing the undulations of the interference fringes given by an arrangement analogous to that of Michelson for measuring apparent stellar diameters (§ 57), and we thus find that it increases proportionally to sec ζ ($\zeta < 65°$) (A. Danjon). These two observational procedures concur in showing that the irregularities of the wave surface are completely independent beyond a distance of some tens of centimeters.

The appearance of the telescopic image depends on the ratio between the turbulence t, measured with an interferometer, and the angular radius ϵ of the central diffraction image, the expression for which is given by the classical theory for an optically perfect objective or mirror of diameter D [9]

$$\epsilon_{(radians)} = 1.22 \; \lambda/D \qquad (10.1)$$

(λ and D evaluated in the same units).   It is more convenient to express the wavelength λ in microns, D in cm and ϵ in seconds of arc. We then have

$$\epsilon = 25'' \cdot \lambda/D. \tag{10.2}$$

Thus for $\lambda = 0.55\,\mu$, $\epsilon = 14''/D$.

The diffraction rings practically disappear for $t \simeq \epsilon$ (for $0''.23$ with $D = 60$ cm, $0''.12$ with $D = 120$ cm).   Sometimes the turbulence at the zenith is less than $0''.10$, but more usually it is several tenths of a second and can surpass $10''$ in a high wind.

On the turbulence are superimposed *accidental refractions* that evolve much more slowly (a complete cycle in 10 to 20 seconds, instead of many cycles per second), and whose amplitude commonly attains $1''$. While turbulence acts in an independent manner for two stars separated by several seconds of arc,[5] the accidental refractions impose displacements between groups of stars in a much more extended field. These accidental refractions can apparently be attributed to the movement of heterogeneous masses of air in the vicinity of the ground.

These atmospheric seeing conditions sometimes hinder photometric measurements a great deal, and they constantly interfere in stellar spectroscopy.   But their influence differs according to the receivers and the methods of measurement, and they depend notably on the *time constant*.   It is therefore necessary to examine it in each particular case.

---

[5] This is why the planets do not twinkle when viewed by the naked eye.

CHAPTER II

STELLAR PHOTOMETRY AND COLORIMETRY

I. PHOTOGRAPHIC MEASUREMENTS

11. Photographic and photovisual magnitudes; color indices

The study of individual stars, such as variables, are today carried out almost exclusively with photoelectric photometry. But photographic measurements still frequently serve for determining from a single plate the stellar magnitudes in a more or less extended field.

Photographic magnitudes (m_{pg}) are measured on the so-called "ordinary" plates (although their use is becoming more and more exceptional), whose spectral sensitivity does not extend beyond 0.50 or 0.51 μ at the long wavelength end. They are therefore concerned with blue, violet and near ultraviolet radiation. The ultraviolet limit is extended toward the short wavelengths when a silvered mirror is substituted for an achromatic objective or an aluminized mirror is substituted for a silvered one. The *zero* of the photographic scale is fixed by Pickering's rule: the stars of spectral type A0 (§ 39) and visual magnitude between 5.5 and 6.5 become, in the mean, equal in photographic magnitude to their visual magnitude.

Photovisual magnitudes (m_{pv}) are measured on orthochromatic plates, sensitive up to about 0.59 μ in the long wavelengths, and used with a yellow filter to eliminate radiation below 0.50 μ. These plates have a maximum sensitivity at about 0.555 μ, which coincides with the maximum sensitivity of the eye for a sufficient illumination of the retina, but which is very much sharper (Fig. 4). Photovisual magnitudes have practically replaced visual magnitudes (m_v); the two scales differ very little when their zero points are brought into coincidence.

The difference

$$C = m_{pg} - m_{pv}$$

between the photographic and photovisual magnitudes, called the *color index*, gives the first indication of a star's color. According to

Pickering's rule, the index must vanish in the mean for A0 stars of the sixth magnitude. Since nearly all stars emit a continuous spectrum rather similar to that of a black body (see Chap. VI), the color index is positive for the stars cooler (redder) than A0, negative for stars hotter (bluer).

Naturally, we can define an infinity of color index systems by isolating different spectral regions by means of colored filters. At Harvard, for example, magnitudes determined from panchromatic plates with blue and with red filters have been compared.

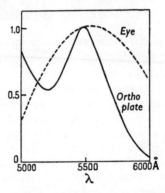

Fig. 4.　Sensitivity curves for the eye and for an orthochromatic plate (measurements by the author, 1928).

12. Photometric measurements of in-focus images

On photographs taken at the focus of refractors or reflectors, the stars show as spots more or less blackened, and more or less extended. Examined with sufficient magnification, these "images" appear as irregular aggregations of silver grains, more crowded together toward the center. The images of the weakest stars visible on a plate taken with a Schmidt telescope of small focal ratio ($n = F/D =$ focal length/diameter $\simeq 2$) have diameters of a score of microns, and on a plate taken with a large parabolic reflector ($n \simeq 6$) they have diameters of at least 30 to 50 μ. It is impossible to measure the optical density at the *interior* of these images, since they are too small and too heterogeneous; therefore, the classical methods of photographic photometry, although still usable for stars of sensible apparent diameter, cannot apply to the stellar photometry of in-focus images.

This difficulty has often been subvented by artificially enlarging the stellar images, for example, by placing the plate slightly in front of or behind the focal plane (extra-focal method), or by moving the plate in a rectangular pattern during the exposure (*Schraffierkassette*), but these procedures, which require a considerably longer exposure, are convenient only for rather bright stars and are only rarely employed. For a long time the measurement of the "diameters" of focal images (poorly defined as they may be) has served for magnitude determinations, but the method is imprecise and lacks sensitivity. Today only the method of Schilt is used.

The photographic image of a star, enlarged by complex diffusion phenomena in the gelatine, is in general much larger than the corresponding diffraction spot [9].

The angular radius of the diffraction image having been calculated in radians from formula (10.1), the linear diameter d of the diffraction spot becomes

$$d = 2\epsilon F = 2.44\lambda F/D = 2.44\lambda n.$$

For a mean wavelength $\lambda = 0.43 \mu$, which corresponds to photographic measurements on "ordinary" plates, the diameter d in microns is expressed essentially by the same number as the focal ratio n: for $n = 2$, $d = 2.1 \mu$; for $n = 6$, $d = 6.3 \mu$; etc. It is only for quite small focal ratios, not useful in photometry, that the diameter of the diffraction spot becomes of the same order of magnitude as the diameter imposed by the photographic plate ($d = 31.5 \mu$ for $n = 30$).

The atmospheric seeing conditions can also contribute to enlarging the stellar image at the focus of large instruments. The diameter imposed by the turbulence is in effect

$$d' = 2tF$$

if the turbulence t is expressed in radians. At the focus of an objective of 2 m focal length, t must reach $1''.5$ or $2''.6$ for d' to become equal to 30 or 50 μ. But, with a focal length of 6 m or of 12 m, t need only surpass $0''.5$ or $0''.25$ for d' to attain 30 μ.

Atmospheric seeing conditions can destroy the images of the stars that are weakest for a given exposure time, but it does not essentially hinder measurements made by Schilt's method.

SCHILT'S METHOD.—Let us illuminate on a photographic plate a circle whose surface S is of the order of magnitude of the star images. Let E_0 be the uniform illumination on the entrance face of the plate. A surface element dS receives the flux $dF_0 = E_0 \, dS$, the entire circle the flux $F_0 = E_0 S$. If T is the transmission factor of the element dS, the flux emerging through it is $dF = TE_0 \, dS$, and the total emergent flux is expressed by

$$F = E_0 \int_S T \, dS.$$

A part of the opacity is necessarily provided by the background fog of the plate (light of the night sky plus chemical fogging). We take this into account by making a similar reading of the plate background in the vicinity of the star. Thus we actually measure the ratio

$$\frac{F}{F_0} = \frac{1}{S} \int_S T \, dS = \bar{T}.$$

This is the mean transmission factor inside the illuminated circle (deducting the background fog).

These measurements are made preferably with a *variable iris photometer*, functioning according to a null method, whose receiver is a photomultiplier tube (§ 17). The tube receives alternately two luminous fluxes originating from the same lamp. The one traverses a graduated absorbing wedge, serving as a calibration, whose initially chosen position for each series of measurements remains invariable throughout the series. The other passes through an iris diaphragm, whose reduced image is projected on the plate by a microscope objective. The equalization of the fluxes is obtained by adjusting the iris opening in a manner that varies the diameter of the illuminated circle on the photograph. The curve relating the surface of the iris (or its logarithm) to the magnitude can thus remain almost rectilinear over an interval of 7 to 8 magnitudes, and the precision of the measurements approaches ± 0.02 magnitudes, or about 2%.[1]

We therefore possess an excellent method of interpolation. We assume to be known, at the beginning, the magnitudes of a certain number of stars in the field, going from the most brilliant to those most faint.[2]

13. Standardization of photographs. North polar sequence and standard magnitudes

Magnitudes can be determined by means of a photoelectric cell associated with a colored filter such that the combination of cell plus

[1] The relative error $\Delta E/E$ of stellar brightness is linked to the absolute error Δm in the magnitude by the relation
$$\Delta E/E = \Delta(\log_e E) = \Delta(\log_{10} E)/\log_{10} e = -0.4 \, \Delta m/\log_{10} e = -0.921 \, \Delta m.$$

[2] Many photographic objectives possess a very limited field of full illumination (vignetting), and for them it may be necessary to determine an empirical correction depending on the distance from the optical axis.

filter has practically the same spectral sensitivity curve as the photographic plate. This method is often used today.

Another procedure, older and purely photographic, consists of weakening in known steps the brightnesses of one or more stars in a field in order to establish the curve relating magnitudes to the photometer readings. The gradation can be accomplished with absorbing screens (which are never rigorously neutral) or by an objective diaphragm. In either case, serious difficulties present themselves. But once this work has been completed for some particular star field, we can establish the calibration curve for another by photographing the standard field on the same plate as the field being studied. All the difficulties of photometric standardization thus lie with the measurements of the standard field, made once and for all. In order to avoid the important and often uncertain corrections for atmospheric absorption, the two fields should be photographed at the same zenith distance.

By virtue of its fixed altitude, the vicinity of the north celestial pole is, for stations in the northern hemisphere, the most favorable choice for the establishment of a magnitude sequence that is useful at every hour of the night throughout the year. Thus considerable efforts have been expended to determine precise stellar magnitudes in the vicinity of the pole.

The *north polar sequence* provides the foundation for the *international system of photographic magnitudes*. Established by Seares (1914–1922) and taking into account observations made at Mt. Wilson, Harvard, Yerkes and other observatories, it includes 96 stars with photographic magnitudes between 2.5 and 20.1, plus a supplementary list of 56 stars. Using the 60-inch telescope at Mt. Wilson, the plate calibrations were effected with diaphragms, some circular and others in the form of sectors, and with fine metallic wires placed in front of the telescope, which produced a weakening measurable in the laboratory.

Comparison with recent photoelectric measurements shows that, as a whole, the precision obtained is of the order of ± 0.02 magnitude. However, a systematic error apparently exists in the scale of the polar sequence, reaching 0.10 magnitude for stars of about sixth photographic magnitude.

In the same way the *international scale of photovisual magnitudes* is fixed by the *north polar sequence of photovisual magnitudes* (Seares), which extends down to the 17th photovisual magnitude. Seares and Joyner (1943) have shown that the color indices in the international system do not vanish in the mean for A0 stars, but for stars a little cooler, of type A5.

Since not all the regions of the sky can be observed at the altitude of the pole, we must derive other magnitude sequences based on the polar sequence, to provide secondary standards. Examples are the Harvard standard regions, distributed between declination $+75°$ and $-90°$, which reach, in the various cases, stars of 15th, 17th or 19th photographic magnitude, with a mean deviation in the order of ± 0.04 or $+0.08$ magnitude. Magnitude sequences have also been very carefully established in certain galactic clusters such as Praesepe and the Pleiades.

The polar photographic and photovisual sequences are affected by the mean atmospheric absorption for the altitude of the pole at Mt. Wilson, about $34°$ (latitude $34° 13'$ N, altitude 1742 m). This fact has no practical significance at a station where the magnitudes in a star field are determined with respect to the sequence, at the altitude of the pole. The brightnesses of the two series of stars are in effect reduced to the same ratio (variable with the station and the night considered).

But the correction which must be made to magnitudes in order to reduce them to above the atmosphere is not the same in the case of photographic and photovisual magnitudes. Let m_{pg}^0, m_{pv}^0 and C^0 be the magnitudes and color index above the atmosphere, Δm_{pg} and Δm_{pv} the photographic and photovisual magnitude losses at the zenith for a station of latitude φ. We measure the color index at the height of the pole, C, by

$$C = m_{pg} - m_{pv} = m_{pg} - m_{pv}^0 + \operatorname{cosec} \varphi(\Delta m_{pg} - \Delta m_{pv})$$
$$= C^0 + \operatorname{cosec} \varphi(\Delta m_{pg} - \Delta m_{pv})$$

which depends on the law of differential absorption $\Delta m_{pg} - \Delta m_{pv}$ at the zenith for the station and for its latitude.

To show the importance of the variation in color index with the air mass, let us suppose that the photographic and photovisual measurements contain only two monochromatic radiations of wavelengths 0.430 and 0.543 μ. The optical density produced at the zenith by molecular diffusion can be evaluated by formula (6.1). We find at sea level for the two radiations, 0.115 and 0.044. The increase in the color index that would result from crossing the air mass M is, under these conditions,

$$\Delta C = 2.5 \, (0.115 - 0.044)M = 0.18M.$$

Color indices have no precise significance except when reduced to above the atmosphere.

14. Equivalent wavelengths and effective wavelengths

To compute a first approximation, it is often convenient to simulate the aforementioned radiation (from a source having a continuous spectrum) over a limited interval by monochromatic radiation of an appropriate wavelength. Let us represent by $e(\lambda)$ the energy distribution in a stellar spectrum, and by $S(\lambda)$ the spectral sensitivity of the receiver, incorporating when necessary the transmission factors of a colored filter in this latter function. The measured stellar brightness, reduced to above the atmosphere, has the expression

$$E = \int e(\lambda) \cdot S(\lambda) \cdot d\lambda,$$

the integral being extended over the domain where the product $e(\lambda) \cdot S(\lambda)$ differs from zero. It can be represented by monochromatic radiation whose wavelength λ_0 is defined by

$$\lambda_0 = \int \lambda \cdot S(\lambda) \cdot d\lambda \Big/ \int S(\lambda) \cdot d\lambda \qquad (14.1)$$

[weighted mean of the wavelengths, where the weights are proportional to $S(\lambda)$].

To the accuracy of the first two terms of a Taylor's series expansion,

$$e(\lambda) = e(\lambda_0) + (\lambda - \lambda_0) \frac{d}{d\lambda} [e(\lambda_0)],$$

we easily verify that E can be written

$$E = e(\lambda_0) \int S(\lambda) \cdot d\lambda. \qquad (14.2)$$

The integral of the second factor is determined only by the constant properties of the receiver. E is therefore proportional to $e(\lambda_0)$ and the magnitude differences measured with the receiver are identical to the differences of the monochromatic magnitudes for the *equivalent wavelength* λ_0. This result is valid only when we can neglect the second derivative $d^2[e(\lambda_0)]/d\lambda^2$ in the spectral interval used. The approximation generally holds for photovisual measurements and photoelectric measurements made with colored filters, in the absence of strong absorption lines.

The relation (14.2) is not true for the rather frequently used *effective wavelength* defined by

$$\lambda_e = \int \lambda \cdot e(\lambda) \cdot S(\lambda) \cdot d\lambda \Big/ \int e(\lambda) \cdot S(\lambda) \cdot d\lambda, \qquad (14.3)$$

in which the energy curve $e(\lambda)$ of the source is involved.

Seares and Joyner have calculated the effective wavelengths corresponding to the international photographic and photovisual magnitudes, representing the stellar energy curves $e(\lambda)$ by those of black bodies with various temperatures, and determining $S(\lambda)$, with the inclusion of atmospheric transmission factors above Mt. Wilson, in the direction of the pole. The values below show that λ_e varies with temperature much less in the case of the more monochromatic photovisual measurements than for photographic measurements. In the latter case, a telescope with an aluminized mirror, reflecting better in the ultraviolet, leads to a smaller λ_e (numbers in parentheses).

T (°K)	Spectrum	$\lambda_e(A)$		
		m_{pv}	m_{pg}	m_{pg}
30,000	B0	5115	4165	(4010)
11,000	A5	5426	4242	(4122)
6,000	G0	5442	4351	(4273)
3,500	M0	5468	4508	(4472)

II. PHOTOELECTRIC MEASUREMENTS

15. Cells used in stellar photometry [22, 23]

The functioning of the so-called *photoemissive cells* used as receivers in stellar photometry from the ultraviolet to the near infrared depends on the photoelectric effect at the surface of semiconductors whose composition includes an alkali metal. The sensitive layer, placed in a good vacuum and raised to a negative potential, plays the role of a cathode. The photons impinging on it release electrons; captured by the anode, these electrons give rise to the photoelectric current. These cells are characterized by a high *quantum efficiency*: with caesium–antimony cathodes, 1 photon out of 10, and sometimes 1 photon out of 4, causes the emission of an electron (an efficiency of 10–25%).

When the cell is exposed to radiation of a constant spectral composition, the intensity of the photoelectric current depends on the potential difference between the anode and cathode, and on the flux received by the cathode. With a constant potential difference, which can be chosen between rather wide limits, the intensity of the photoelectric current is rigorously proportional to the flux. This property is one of the principal advantages of vacuum cells in photometry, because their use completely eliminates the standardization scales that are always required in photographic measurements.

SPECTRAL SENSITIVITY.—Depending on the nature of the cathode, the cells have very different spectral sensitivities (Fig. 5). The potassium hydride cells, which for a long time were used almost exclusively, are sensitive from about 0.29 to 0.59 μ, with a maximum around 0.435 μ. The caesium–antimony cell (Cs–Sb), widely used today, is sensitive from the ultraviolet to the red, with a maximum around 0.40 μ. The cells of caesium oxide on silver (Cs–O–Ag) show a sensitivity curve with two maxima, the first below 0.40 μ and the second near 0.80 μ, and extend up to about 1.2 μ.

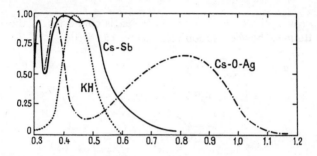

FIG. 5. SENSITIVITY CURVES OF COMMON CELLS.

TOTAL SENSITIVITY.—The total sensitivity of present-day *vacuum cells*, illuminated by a lamp having a tungsten filament with a color temperature of 2870° K (§ 46), is generally in the order of 15 to 20 microamperes per lumen for the Cs–O–Ag cells and about 20 to 100 μamp per lumen for the Cs–Sb cells.[3]

DARK CURRENT.—A cell with the voltage applied in complete darkness delivers a weak current owing to leakage in the cell and to the thermionic effect.

Exterior leakage can be greatly reduced by sealing the cell in a box carefully desiccated by activated aluminum. Often a grounded guard ring is placed around the electrical terminals.

The thermionic effect depends on the nature of the cathode, and rises very rapidly with temperature. At room temperature it is very small for potassium cells, but always appreciable for cathodes containing caesium. Cs–O–Ag cells must be refrigerated to −60° or

[3] It is notably larger for *gas cells* where the photoelectron released from the cathode ionizes by collision the argon held in the tube under a pressure in the order of 0.2 cm of mercury. Each photoelectron can ionize many argon atoms, intensifying the current by a factor of 5 to 10. But with gas cells the proportionality of the current to the flux is no longer assured.

$-80°$ C (with dry ice, for example), but it is also worthwhile to refrigerate Cs–Sb cells to below $0°$ C.

16. Measurement of the photoelectric current

The measurable flux in stellar photometry is generally very small. A star with a brightness of E lux, observed with a telescope of diameter D meters and whose transmission factor is T, sends to the cathode the flux

$$\mathscr{F} = \frac{\pi}{4} D^2 TE.$$

Moreover, the stellar brightness in lux is connected to the visual magnitude m_v by the relation (1.2), so we can write:

$$\log \mathscr{F} = \log \frac{\pi}{4} + \log T + 2 \log D - 0.4(m_v + 14.2)$$

$$= \log T + 2 \log D - 0.4 m_v - 5.785.$$

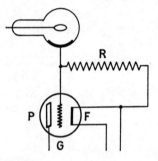

FIG. 6.   SCHEMATIC OF A RESISTANCE AMPLIFIER.

With a telescope of 0.80 m diameter and a negligible central obscuration, we find, in taking $T = 0.85$ (two mirrors and a lens), that the cell receives a flux of $2.7 \cdot 10^{-11}$ lumens from a star of 11th magnitude.

A cell having a total sensitivity of 80 μamp/lumen would then give a photoelectric current of intensity $2 \cdot 10^{-15}$ amp.   This gives only the order of magnitude, since the sensitivity of the cell is by convention evaluated for radiation corresponding to a color temperature of $2870°$ K, less than the color temperature of the majority of stars (§ 48). But the rough calculation suffices to demonstrate that the photoelectric current cannot be measured without great amplification.

Figure 6 shows a simplified scheme for an amplifier using resistance.

The photoelectric current of intensity i, in flowing through the large resistance R, creates a variation of $\Delta V = Ri$ in the potential of the grid G in the triode; the potential is negative with respect to the filament F. A significant variation results in the plate current flowing in the tube from the anode P to the cathode F. In practice, an *electrometer tube* of high resistance replaces the triode.

The use of a resistance amplifier unfortunately augments the fluctuations that are always present in the photoelectric current. This *noise* has a double origin. It arises in part from the irregular emission of electrons by the cathode ("shot" effect), since only about 1 photon in 10 causes the emission of an electron. It also arises from the completely irregular character of the voltage that the random thermal agitation of the electrons produces throughout the conductor (Johnson effect). The mean square of this voltage is proportional to the absolute temperature and the resistance of the conductor. With the load resistance in the order of 10^9 to 10^{12} ohms, the Johnson effect greatly overpowers the shot effect, and the *signal-to-noise ratio* is greatly diminished.

17. Use of photomultipliers

The use of photomultipliers is, in this regard, much more advantageous. Certain substances, when struck by electrons with sufficient energy, emit many secondary electrons. In photomultipliers, the electrons arising from the cathode are accelerated in the vacuum and concentrated by an electric or magnetic field on an initial multiplier target or *dynode*. The secondary electrons emitted from it are in turn accelerated and concentrated on a second dynode, and so on. If each target multiplies the number of electrons it receives by a factor G, after encountering p dynodes, the intensity of the photoelectric current is multiplied by G^p. The *multiplication factor G* can be about 4 to 5 for targets whose plate is a continuous surface (such as the RCA 1P21 photomultiplier), or about 2 to 2.5 for grids or metallic meshes (as in the multipliers of Lallemand).

The 1P21 photomultiplier of the Radio Corporation of America (RCA), frequently used in stellar photometry, contains 9 stages of electrostatic multiplication. With $G = 5$, for a potential difference of about 100 volts between each stage, we obtain a total gain of around $2 \cdot 10^6$. The total sensitivity of the Cs–Sb photocathode being about 20 μamp/lumen, the sensitivity of the multiplier reaches 40 amp/lumen (although the cell cannot support currents greater than 10^{-4} amp without deterioration).

Figure 7 shows the schematic arrangement of Lallemand's

photomultiplier.   The surfaces for the secondary emission, made of a magnesium–silver alloy in shaped foil screens, are raised to potentials of $+V$, $+2V$, $+3V$, etc., with respect to the cathode by means of a potentiometer with a regulated power supply.   Their form has been designed to assure good focusing, and they play the role of electrostatic lenses.   The cells are generally constructed with 19 or 20 stages of internal multiplication.   With $G = 2.45$, $p = 19$, and an inter-stage potential difference of $V = 102$ volts (which would gain no advantage in being increased), the total gain surpasses $2 \cdot 10^7$.   The sensitivity of the cathode being about $80\ \mu$amp/lumen, the entire assembly attains the enormous value of 1600 amp/lumen.   However, one must avoid making the cell's output greater than 10^{-7} amp.

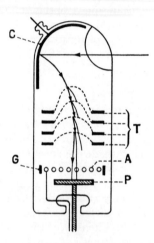

FIG. 7.   DIAGRAM OF A PHOTOMULTIPLIER.
C, cathode; T, multiplier network; P, potentiometer with stabilized
power supply; A, anode; G, guard ring.

At the terminals of the photomultiplier, the current is already intense enough so that we can be content with a moderate amplification (for example, in the order of 10^2 or 10^3), possible with a resistance not too great and with very good stability, or we can even eliminate all amplification.   The fluctuations then arise principally from the shot effect, which cannot be avoided.   Provided that the multiplication factor G per dynode is greater than about 2, the signal-to-noise ratio is practically undiminished by successive dynodes.   *The reduction*

of the Johnson effect and the practically instantaneous response are the essential
qualities of multipliers for the measurement of very weak fluxes.[4]

Figure 8 shows schematically the arrangement used in many French
observatories. The current leaving the multiplier M is transported
under high impedance to an *impedance transformer A* where it is modified
in such a manner as to produce a voltage of several millivolts (resistance
in the order of 200 ohms) at the terminals of a recording millivoltmeter

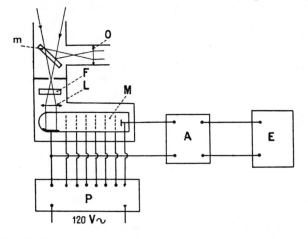

FIG. 8. SCHEMATIC ASSEMBLY OF A PHOTOELECTRIC PHOTOMETER.
m, removable mirror; O, eyepiece; F, filter; L, field lens; M, multiplier;
P, potentiometer with a stabilized power supply; A, impedance transformer;
E, recording millivoltmeter.

E. The resistance at the terminals where the voltage is measured can
be divided in order to vary the sensitivity, and the introduction of
various capacitances allows a modification of the time constant
(ordinarily 2 or 3 seconds). The lateral eyepiece O and the movable
mirror m serve for centering the star inside a diaphragm placed in the

---

[4] When the flux received is extremely small, the *quantum fluctuation*, associated
with the discontinuity of luminous emission, will itself produce fluctuations even
in a perfect cell, where the arrival of each photon will produce the emission of
an electron.

To measure a very weak flux, we can, with an instrument that measures the
instantaneous response, count the impulses received during a sufficient period;
the apparatus is then functioning as a photon counter. We must, of course,
deduct the number of impulses received during the same time when the cell is
not illuminated (the dark current), or, if stars are being measured, when the
cell receives only the background light of the sky [21, 32].

focal plane.   After traversing the filter F, the lens L projects the image
of the telescope mirror on the cathode, so that the same part of the
cathode is always used.

Before or after each reading on a star, it is necessary to make a
reading on the sky near the star, in order to deduct the deviation
given by the sky from that given by the star, with the same diaphragm,
sensitivity and color filter.

It is the light of the night sky that effectively limits the observation
of faint stars.   For example, at the Cassegrain focus of the 80-cm
telescope at the Haute Provence Observatory $(F = 12$ m$)$, the star
image is isolated with a diaphragm 2 mm in diameter, corresponding
to a solid angle of $\omega = 2.16 \cdot 10^{-8}$ steradian.   The magnitude m of the
portion of sky seen with this angle can be calculated by the formula
(3.2), if the mean magnitude m_1 of 1 steradian of sky (without moon-
light) is known.   With $m_1 = -4.4$ (or 13.3 per 1' square) in blue
light, we find $m = 14.8$.   The presence of a 15th magnitude star
inside the diaphragm would thus essentially double the deviation
produced by the sky.   We can accept this as quite near the limiting
magnitude for stars observable in these conditions.

The precision of the measurements is often limited by variations in
atmospheric absorption or by turbulence.   When the atmosphere is
steady and the images quiet, it attains 1% or 0.01 magnitude.   But
when the mean turbulence t (§ 10) is in the order of several seconds of
a degree, the measurements become uncertain, because a non-
negligible fraction of the flux is rejected from the diaphragm, since
part of it is more than 15″ from the axis.   This is why it is rarely
possible to work with such a tiny diaphragm.

18. Photoelectric color indices.   3- and 6-color photometry

Let us measure successively with the same cell the brightnesses E
and E' of the same star, isolating two different spectral regions by
means of colored filters.   The photoelectric color index is, by
definition, the magnitude difference corresponding to the ratio E/E':

$$C = m - m' = -2.5 \log (E/E').$$

It depends simultaneously on the energy distribution of the stellar
spectrum, the spectral sensitivity of the cell, the transmission curves of
the filters, and the transmission factors of the atmosphere.   The
numbers obtained have a precise significance, however, if we always
work with the same cell and same filters, and if we reduce the stellar
brightnesses E and E' to above the atmosphere (§ 13).

Color indices are determined to much greater precision with a photoelectric cell than by photography, very often to about ± 0.02 magnitude. Furthermore, notable variations in atmospheric absorption are less to be feared since the measurements with the two filters succeed one another within several minutes.

Such measurements were at first made with a potassium cell in association with blue and yellow filters (Bottlinger and W. Becker; Stebbins, Huffer and Whitford). With a Cs–O–Ag cell color indices between the red and near infrared have also been measured (Hall, Bennett). The very extensive research of Stebbins and his collaborators on the hot stars of type B (§ 34) have uncovered very important information about interstellar absorption (§ 50). Nevertheless the two spectral regions for which these measurements were carried out were still rather close and largely infringed on one another.

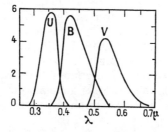

FIG. 9. THREE-COLOR PHOTOMETRY (U–B–V).
Sensitivity of the cell associated with three filters (in arbitrary units), having equal energy in all wavelengths.

Great progress has been realized by using Cs–Sb photomultipliers. H. L. Johnson and W. W. Morgan have made very precise measurements in 3 colors with a 1P21 tube associated with 3 color filters: ultraviolet (U), blue (B) and yellow (V). Figure 9 shows the sensitivity curves of the cell associated with each of these filters (equivalent wavelengths $\lambda_0 = 3499, 4425, 5539$ A).

By convention, the color indices B–V and U–B are zero above the atmosphere for the mean of 6 dwarf stars of spectral type A0: α Lyr, γ UMa, α CrB, 109 Vir, γ Oph and HR 3314.

Johnson and Morgan have published a catalogue containing magnitudes of 290 stars measured with a yellow filter (V), and their B–V and U–B color indices, all reduced to above the atmosphere (1953). These standard stars have been chosen to include all spectral types, and in each type, all the luminosity classes (that is to say, stars of very diverse absolute magnitudes: see § 39). Moreover, they are not sensibly affected by interstellar absorption. Naturally these

standard stars are scattered over all the sky observable in the northern
hemisphere, but the catalogue is augmented by sequences in auxiliary
regions chosen in 4 galactic clusters: Praesepe, the Pleiades, M36
and NGC 2362.[5]

The V magnitudes, determined with a yellow filter, coincide almost
exactly with those of the photovisual magnitudes on the international system. But the new photometric system presents certain
advantages over the old ones (in addition to being reduced to above
the atmosphere): the polar sequence does not include stars of such
diverse categories and, further, the region of the north pole is reddened
by an absorbing layer. Thus for several years now there has been an
attempt to reduce all photometric measurements to the U–B–V
system of Johnson and Morgan.[6]

In a series of studies pursued since 1942, Stebbins and Whitford,
working with a caesium on silver photomultiplier, have isolated with
filters 6 spectral regions that more or less overlap one another
($\lambda_0 = 0.350, 0.422, 0.488, 0.570, 0.719, 1.03\ \mu$). Such measurements
are already equivalent to a rather coarse spectrograph. Now many
more monochromatic interference filters (with pass bands of 50 to
200 A) are beginning to be used for an analogous purpose, and these
measurements would appear to be an important development (§ 54).

19. Use of lead sulfide cells

The photoconductive lead sulfide cell, whose resistance varies when
it is illuminated, is at present the most sensitive receiver between 1
and 2.5 μ. Its resistance is relatively weak (10^5 to 10^6 ohms) and its
noise is high. The amplification is therefore made with alternating
current. The light is modulated with a frequency of several hundreds
of cycles per second by means of a rotating disk that has regular
rectangular teeth at its periphery. The current, having flowed
through the cell, is sent through an amplifier with a rather narrow

[5] Star clusters and nebulae are designated by their serial number in the
Messier catalogue (M) (Paris, 1784) or in Dreyer's much more complete *New
General Catalogue* ... (NGC) (1890) and its extensions, the *Index Catalogue* (IC)
(1895, 1910).

[6] A 3-color system is indispensable for reducing to the same scale a series of
independent measurements made with receivers that have slightly different
spectral sensitivities. The correction that must be made to a color index
depends, in fact, on two parameters: for hot stars of types O, B and A, on the
spectral type and the interstellar absorption; for the less hot stars, on the spectral
type and absolute magnitude. On this account it is necessary to have two color
indices available for making the corrections (see § 51).

pass band that matches the modulation frequency, before being detected and then measured, either with a galvanometer or with a recording millivoltmeter. The response is not exactly linear.

Certain cells acquire a good sensitivity only at low temperatures and must be refrigerated to $-80°$ C by dry ice. Others are usable at room temperature, but it is always better to maintain a constant and rather low temperature ($< 0°$ C). Even in the region of their maximum sensitivity, the performances of Pb–S cells are very inferior to those of photoemissive cells below 1 μ, and, as a matter of fact, their use is at present limited to the study of rather bright stars.

Fellgett (1951) reached the 6th magnitude in total light for yellow solar-type stars, at the focus of a 36-inch telescope. With a 120-cm (47-inch) telescope, Mme. Lunel (1955–57) has reached red stars of the 8th visual magnitude, eliminating wavelengths below 0.74 μ. With various colored or interference filters, it is possible to isolate several narrower regions in the near infrared. Undoubtedly lead telluride cells will soon permit the measurements to be extended up to 4 μ.

III. THERMAL MEASUREMENTS.
RADIOMETRIC AND BOLOMETRIC MAGNITUDES

20. Interest and difficulty of thermal measurements

Let $e(\lambda) \cdot d\lambda$ be the energy brightness above the atmosphere in a very narrow spectral region $d\lambda$, produced by a star. With a thermal receiver (radiometer, bolometer or thermocouple), considered as equally sensitive to all radiation, we could measure, above the atmosphere, the total energy brightness:

$$E_b = \int_0^\infty e(\lambda) \cdot d\lambda,$$

(expressed in watts $\cdot$ cm^{-2} or in ergs $\cdot$ sec$^{-1} \cdot$ cm^{-2}).

For any selective receiver, we have the measure of brightness

$$E = \int_0^\infty e(\lambda) \cdot S(\lambda) \cdot d\lambda,$$

where $S(\lambda)$ represents the spectral sensitivity of the receiver (filter included), and, if necessary, incorporates the transmission factors of the atmosphere in the direction of the star. The effect of the atmosphere can be removed by reducing the measurements to above it, but the spectral sensitivity of the receiver necessarily plays a part. It would be much more interesting to evaluate the total energy brightness E_b, which depends only on the star, but the lack of sensitivity of thermal receivers becomes an obstacle to its determination most of the time.

In order to have an idea of the size of the quantities to be measured, let us consider a star whose energy curve is practically identical to that of the sun, such as the A component of the double 16 Cyg (spectrum G2, luminosity class V, § 39). Its photovisual magnitude is $+5.96$, that of the sun -26.73. The ratio of stellar brightnesses is then such that:

$$\log (E_*/E_\odot) = -0.4(5.96 + 26.73) = -13.08,$$

from which

$$E_*/E_\odot = 8.4 \cdot 10^{-14}.$$

Now the energy brightness produced by the sun at the zenith at Mount Wilson is about 0.11 watts·cm^{-2} (or 1.6 cal·gr·cm^{-2} min^{-1}). Under the same conditions the star gives

$$E = 9.2 \cdot 10^{-15} \text{ watts·cm}^{-2}$$

$$= 1.3 \cdot 10^{-13} \text{ cal·gr·cm}^{-2} \text{ min}^{-1}.$$

Let us concentrate the flux received by a perfectly reflecting mirror of 2.5 m diameter on a perfectly absorbing little metallic screen, of mass 0.1 mg and specific heat 0.1. If all heat losses are eliminated, the temperature of the screen will rise $6.5 \cdot 10^{-4}$ ° C in 1 minute.

Of all the stars, Betelgeuse (α Ori, type M2) produces the greatest energy brightness for the zenith at Mt. Wilson ($5.4 \cdot 10^{-12}$ ergs·sec^{-1}· cm^{-2}). The energy brightness of Sirius (α CMa, type A1) scarcely surpasses 2/3 of that, although its visual brightness equals 10 times that of Betelgeuse. But, above the atmosphere, the two stars would produce essentially the same energy brightness, because the light of Sirius is rich in ultraviolet radiation absorbed by the atmosphere.

21. Thermoelectric measurements and radiometric magnitudes

Pettit and Nicholson used mainly thermocouples of bismuth joined to a bismuth–tin alloy. The wires had a diameter of 0.03 mm, and the two junctions had a diameter of 0.5 mm and a mass of 0.035 mg. The junctions were placed side by side in a vacuum tube provided with a window of glass, quartz, fluorite or rock salt. The image of the star was sent alternately to each junction, in order to double the deviation of the recording galvanometer. The sky radiation was the same on the two junctions and was automatically compensated, even in broad daylight.

With the 100-inch telescope at Mt. Wilson, Pettit and Nicholson measured more than 200 stars (1928), the weakest being about 3rd visual magnitude for the whitest, but reaching to the 12th for the reddest. Many of these were also observed through a water cell, 1 cm thick with quartz windows, which was transparent from 0.3 to 1.4 μ but absorbed the infrared beyond this. The absorption by the window was taken into account when it was glass or quartz, and the measured brightnesses were reduced to the zenith at Mt. Wilson by Bouguer's method.[7]

With the energy brightnesses thus obtained, Pettit and Nicholson set up the corresponding *radiometric magnitudes* m_r, which, by convention, are taken equal to the visual magnitudes for the A0 stars. The *heat index* is by definition the difference between the visual and radiometric magnitudes:

$$H.I. = m_v - m_r.$$

Zero in the mean for A0 stars, it takes greater positive values as the stars become cooler, just as the color indices do.

These astronomers also evaluated the correction Δm_r, which must be subtracted from the radiometric magnitudes to reduce them to above the atmosphere. They took into account principally the absorption bands of water vapor that cut deeply into the infrared spectrum. The correction Δm_r also includes the loss of light in the reflection at the mirrors, which varies with the wavelength.

22. Bolometric magnitudes

In the absence of the possibility of directly measuring the energy brightnesses for the majority of stars, we propose to convert the brightnesses E_0 measured with a selective receiver and reduced to above the atmosphere, to energy brightnesses E_b. It is necessary to have the functions $e(\lambda)$ and $S(\lambda)$ for this. The calculations have been made from the visual or photovisual measurements, by using the sensitivity curve of the eye or that of the orthochromatic plate with a yellow filter. It was at first assumed that the stars radiate like black bodies of known temperature (Hertzsprung, Eddington, Pike). Kuiper (1938) obtained probably more correct values by using

---

[7] The application of this method to a rather extended spectral domain is very risky. But the corrections were small, the stars having been observed as close as possible to the meridian.

theoretical energy curves $e(\lambda)$, calculated by assuming a known composition of stellar atmospheres.

We define a system of magnitudes called *bolometric* corresponding to the energy brightness E_b above the atmosphere, by the relation

$$m_b = -2.5 \log E_b + k,$$

where k is an arbitrary constant.

The photovisual magnitudes being themselves defined by

$$m_{pv} = -2.5 \log E_{pv} + c,$$

the difference $m_b - m_{pv}$ equals

$$m_b - m_{pv} = -2.5 \log (E_b/E_{pv}) + (k - c).$$

The ratio E_b/E_{pv} attains its value closest to unity when the maximum of the energy curve coincides with the maximum of the sensitivity curve of the orthochromatic plate ($\lambda \simeq 0.55 \mu$), which is produced by a temperature in the vicinity of $6500°$ K. Then k is chosen such that the difference $m_b - m_{pv}$ is zero. Therefore, for all temperatures either higher or lower than $6500°$ K, the *bolometric correction BC = $m_b - m_{pv}$* is negative.

To the apparent bolometric magnitudes there naturally correspond the *absolute bolometric magnitudes M_b*. Through the relation (2.3), valid in the absence of absorption in space, we always have

$$M_b - M_{pv} = m_b - m_{pv} = BC.$$

(A similar extension can be made in the case of radiometric magnitudes.)

Table I gives, on the left side, the theoretical bolometric corrections of Kuiper. Here the choice of *effective temperatures* (§ 61) corresponds, according to Morgan and Keenan, to the principal spectral types to be described in Chapters IV and V. This correction is rather poorly determined for low temperature stars, and Kuiper there prefers to use the radiometric magnitudes of Pettit and Nicholson, reduced to above the atmosphere. The coincidence of the two scales is assured by the empirical relation

$$m_b = m_r - \Delta m_r + 0.62.$$

In this it is necessary to distinguish the stars of lesser luminous intensity (called *main sequence MS*, § 38) from those whose absolute visual magnitude is in the vicinity of $M_{pv} = 0$ (giants) or of $M_{pv} = -4$ (supergiants). The empirical bolometric corrections are given in the upper right-hand part of Table I. However, the correspondence between the absolute photovisual magnitude and the spectral type is so direct along the main sequence after $M_v = +3.0$ that we can evaluate the bolometric correction as a function of absolute magnitude without taking the spectral type into account (lower right-hand part of Table I).

TABLE I
BOLOMETRIC CORRECTIONS

Theoretical corrections			Empirical corrections			
					BC (magn)	
Spectrum	T_e (°K)	BC (magn)	Spectrum	MS	$M = 0$	$M = -4$
	50,000	−4.3	F5	−0.04	−0.08	−0.12
	40,000	−3.8	G0	−0.06	−0.25	−0.42
	30,000	−3.12	G5	−0.10	−0.39	−0.65
B0	25,000	−2.69	K0	−0.11	−0.54	−0.93
B1	22,500	−2.45	K3	−0.31	−0.89	−1.35
B2	20,300	−2.20	K5	−0.85	−1.35	−1.86
B3	18,000	−1.94	M0	−1.43	−1.55	−2.2
B5	15,600	−1.60	M5		−3.4	
B6.5	14,000	−1.35				
B8	12,800	−1.14				
B9	11,800	−0.93		*Main sequence*		
A0	11,000	−0.78				
A1	10,300	−0.62	M_{pv}		BC (magn)	
A2	9,700	−0.51				
A5	8,700	−0.34	+3.0		−0.05	
F0	7,600	−0.13	+4.0		−0.05	
F2	7,000	−0.01	+5.0		−0.06	
	6,500	0.00	+6.0		−0.12	
	6,000	−0.06	+7.0		−0.51	
	5,000	−0.34	+8.0		−0.95	
	4,500	−0.65	+9.0		−1.40	
	4,000	(−1.3)	+10.0		−1.85	

CHAPTER III

ASTRONOMICAL SPECTROGRAPHS

23. Slit spectrographs and objective prisms

Celestial spectra are photographed with two types of equipment: *slit spectrographs* and *slitless spectrographs*; the simplest example of the latter is the *objective prism* (or objective grating).

SLIT SPECTROGRAPHS.—Astronomical slit spectrographs are in principle identical to laboratory spectrographs [23]. They consist of a slit at the focus of an objective collimator O_1 (Fig. 10), a dispersion

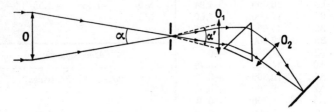

FIG. 10. DIAGRAM OF AN ASTRONOMICAL SLIT SPECTROGRAPH.
For observations of stars, one should have $\alpha \leqslant \alpha'$;
for observations of extended sources, $\alpha > \alpha'$.

system formed of one or several prisms or even of a plane grating, and finally a camera objective O_2, which forms the image of the spectrum on the plate.

Gratings, formerly reserved for the study of the brightest objects and particularly the sun, are today generally used in astrophysics because one can concentrate 70% of the incident light into a single spectrum around a predetermined wavelength by "blazing" the grating, that is, by giving the rulings a particular slant [6]. Figure 11 represents a reflection grating by a saw-tooth pattern, resembling a series of identical plane mirrors, each of width c, making the angle α with the plane of the grating. According to the elementary theory, for an angle of incidence i, the maxima of the diffraction pattern for the wavelength λ correspond to the diffraction angles i' such that

$$c(\sin i' - \sin i) = 2c \sin \frac{i' - i}{2} \cos \frac{i' + i}{2} = p\lambda,$$

where p is an integer. These maxima are especially intense when

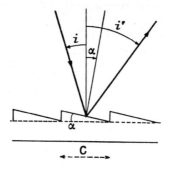

F<small>IG</small>. 11.

they are produced by an ordinary reflection of the elementary mirrors, that is to say, for

$$i' - i = 2\alpha.$$

The wavelength λ for which the light is concentrated in the spectrum of order p is therefore

$$\lambda = \frac{2c}{p} \sin \alpha \cos \frac{i' + i}{2}.$$

With normal incidence, for example, ($i = 0$, $i' = 2\alpha$), we have

$$\lambda = \frac{c}{p} \sin 2\alpha.$$

For $c = \frac{5}{3}$ of a micron (600 lines per mm) and $\alpha = 18°$, the maximum concentration is produced in the first order for $\lambda = 0.98\ \mu$ and, in the second order, for $\lambda = 0.49\ \mu$. Often replica gratings are used, made of a plastic material molded against a metal grating and then aluminized. One can also make copies that function by transmission and present analogous properties.

In the spectrograph diagrammed in Figure 12, the collimator is a small Cassegrain telescope functioning in reverse. It is provided with a transmission grating and a spherical mirror whose aberrations are corrected by two spherical lenses. Since the field is not planar, the spectrum is photographed on a thin plate suitably curved, or on a film.

The spectrograph slit is placed at the focus of a reflector and receives the image of the star being studied. (Refractors are inconvenient by reason of their secondary spectrum: only two radiations, of different wavelengths, can be focused simultaneously at a point on the slit.) The focusing of the image and the guiding during the exposure are assured by means of a *slit viewer*, a sort of elbow microscope that receives the rays reflected from the perfectly polished jaws of the slit, whose planes are inclined with respect to the optical axis. In the case of a prism spectrograph, one can also use for the guiding the light reflected from the entrance face of the first prism, for a sufficiently bright star. Then one can make use of a small telescope equipped with a reticle, focused for infinity.

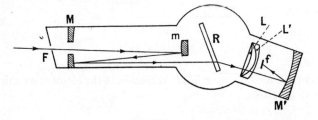

FIG. 12. STELLAR SPECTROGRAPH WITH A GRATING.
F, slit; m, hyperbolic mirror; M, parabolic mirror; R, grating;
L L', correcting lenses; M', spherical mirror; f, film.

Laboratory spectrographs are constructed to work always in the same position, in a place with little temperature variation. The spectrographs fastened to the end of a telescope must be held together in a rigid assembly, in order to work without deformation in all positions. Their mechanical construction must be carefully designed so as to avoid flexure.

The temperature variations inside a dome exposed to solar radiation during the day and progressively cooled during the night are also very troublesome. They not only distort the metallic parts by contraction, but the variations they cause in the refractive index of the lenses and prisms contaminate the purity of the spectra in the course of long nocturnal exposures. For this reason it is necessary to place the spectrograph in a constant-temperature enclosure. In the largest telescopes these difficulties have been greatly reduced by sending the light down the hollow polar axis of the equatorial mounting to the slit of a fixed spectrograph at the *coudé* focus, placed in a constant-temperature laboratory.

SLITLESS SPECTROGRAPHS.—An objective prism is simply constituted by a prism, which receives a bundle of parallel rays coming from a star (Fig. 13), and by an objective, which gives a stellar spectrum in its

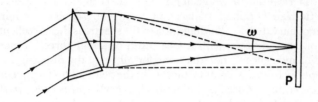

FIG. 13.   DIAGRAM OF AN OBJECTIVE PRISM.

focal plane.   This is essentially an ordinary spectrograph with the collimator and slit suppressed—parts that can be dispensed with since the rays in the bundle are already parallel.   An analogous setup can be made with a grating.

To obtain a given linear dispersion, one sets two parameters: the angular dispersion of the prism and the focal length of the objective. When it is necessary to cover an objective of a foot or more in diameter, it is advantageous to choose a prism with a small angle (several

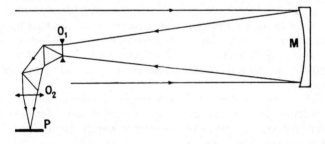

FIG. 14.   DIAGRAM OF A SLITLESS SPECTROGRAPH MOUNTED ON A REFLECTOR.

degrees), for which the glass can more easily be homogeneous and which is also, for equal surfaces, less absorbent than for a large angle prism.   It can also be convenient to use prisms with dimensions much smaller than those of the objective (for ultraviolet studies, with quartz prisms).   We can produce a parallel bundle of rays from those reflected from a telescope mirror, by using a diverging lens O_1 placed in front of a train of prisms (Fig. 14).   If the power of this lens is equal in absolute value to that of lens O_2 serving as the objective, the combination is achromatic.

Wide field objective prisms permit the simultaneous photography of the spectra of a great number of stars, with a weak or moderate dispersion.   For an objective, we often use a Schmidt camera, formed by a spherical mirror whose aberrations are corrected by means of an aspheric plate of thin glass placed in the neighborhood of the mirror's center of curvature.   The definition of the spectra is then excellent in a field of many degrees, with a focal ratio of about three.   Since the angle of incidence is not the same for all stars, the dispersion varies perceptibly from one point to another in the field.   This inconvenience is considerably reduced by Fehrenbach's *objective prism with normal field* (Fig. 15).   It includes two identical prisms of barium-crown, on

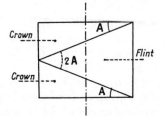

FIG. 15.   NORMAL FIELD PRISM ($A = 18°.66$).

opposite sides of a flint prism with a double angle, so that the combination constitutes a plate with parallel faces.   The indices of the two glasses are chosen to obtain direct vision for a determined radiation (4220 A), at the same time preserving a sufficiently large residual dispersion.

With slitless spectrographs, the positioning and guiding require the use of an auxiliary refractor rigidly fastened to the spectrograph, to prevent differential flexure between the two instruments.

24. Image brightness of astronomical spectrographs

CASE OF A POINT SOURCE.—Let us now suppose that we photograph with an objective prism a star that emits only a bright line spectrum. Each monochromatic image has a diameter much larger than that of a diffraction spot (§ 12).   Now the emulsion acts as if it were formed of discontinuous elements a score of microns in diameter (on the usual plates), and, in the absence of atmospheric disturbances, the monochromatic flux $\mathscr{F}$ traversing the objective prism is practically concentrated in a single one of these elements. The blackening of the plate thus depends solely on the flux $\mathscr{F}$, given by the expression

$$\mathscr{F} = T \cdot E \cdot S. \qquad (24.1)$$

E is the monochromatic stellar brightness for the radiation considered, T the instrumental transmission factor for the same wavelength, and S is the surface area of the objective (covered entirely by the prism). *The flux is therefore proportional to the area of the objective, but independent of focal length.*[1]

If, however, the star emits a continuous spectrum—the usual case— its stellar brightness in a small interval $d\lambda$ can be represented by $e(\lambda)\, d\lambda$. Let $\delta = \partial l/\partial \lambda$ be the linear dispersion, variable with wavelength; the spectral interval $d\lambda$ which covers an element dl of the emulsion will be given by

$$d\lambda = \frac{dl}{\delta}. \qquad (24.2)$$

The flux received by this element can therefore be written

$$d\mathscr{F} = T \cdot S \cdot e(\lambda) \cdot \frac{dl}{\delta}. \qquad (24.3)$$

For a given emulsion (with dl fixed) the flux is still proportional to the surface area of the objective, but also inversely proportional to the linear dispersion.

When we use a slit spectrograph, all the flux going through the collimator is again concentrated on an element of the emulsion. Therefore it is important that all the flux received by the objective or mirror which projects the stellar image on the slit should traverse the collimator lens. Thus the focal ratio of the collimator *must at least equal* that of the objective (Fig. 10). This condition fulfilled, the flux received by an element of the emulsion will be expressed in the same manner as for an objective prism, and formulas (24.1) and (24.3) still hold. However, the transmission factor T has a smaller value. Neither the focal length nor the focal ratio of the objective comes into consideration, but only its surface area S.

CASE OF AN EXTENDED SOURCE.—Objective prisms can still be useful

---

[1] There is not, in reality, a star giving *only* a line spectrum, but in certain cases (*novae* in the nebular stage), the continuum can be very weak with respect to the lines. The result applies also to planetary nebulae of very small apparent diameter, photographed with a short-focus objective prism. If, for example, the focal length is $F = 50$ cm, it suffices for the apparent diameter of the nebula to be less than $5''$ for its monochromatic images to measure less than 10 microns.

when the celestial object under investigation emits a line spectrum, as the gaseous nebulae; in contrast, a continuous spectrum would be completely confused.   Let us take B as the monochromatic luminance of the nebula, whose image covers an extended region of the plate. The blackening now depends on the flux received per unit surface, that is to say, on the brightness E at the plate, which is written, according to (3.1), as

$$E = T \cdot B \cdot \omega, \qquad (24.4)$$

where ω designates the solid angle containing the rays that fall on one point of the plate (Fig. 13).   *Therefore the focal ratio of the objective determines exclusively (along with the transmission factor) the instrumental image brightness for extended objects emitting a line spectrum.*

The brightness at the plate retains the same expression when we use a slit spectrograph.   If the source then emits a continuous spectrum characterized by its luminance $b(\lambda)$, the brightness dE produced on the plate by the spectral interval $d\lambda$ is

$$dE = T \cdot \omega \cdot b(\lambda) \cdot d\lambda.$$

The interval $d\lambda$ being considered here includes the width dl of the slit's image on the plate.   It is still represented by (24.2).   Thus we have

$$dE = T \cdot \omega \cdot b(\lambda) \cdot \frac{dl}{\delta}. \qquad (24.5)$$

The brightness at the plate, always proportional to the solid angle ω, is inversely proportional to the linear dispersion δ.   When the focal ratio $n = F/D$ is rather large (for a small objective opening)

$$\omega = \pi D^2/4F^2 = \pi/4n^2$$

and the brightness is inversely proportional to the square of the focal ratio.

In order to interpret correctly the spectrogram from an extended source, it is desirable to photograph only the fully illuminated portion of the slit.   The collimator aperture must in this case be smaller than the projection of the objective (Fig. 10), and it must become still smaller as the size of the extended source increases.   Neither the diameter, focal length, nor focal ratio of the objective influence the image brightness at the plate.

INFLUENCE OF ATMOSPHERIC DISTURBANCES.—When the stellar images are enlarged by turbulence (§ 10), spectra taken with an objective prism are more or less smeared out.   Thus poor seeing can prevent the use of an objective prism with a large focal length.

With a slit spectrograph, the definition of the spectrum is never altered by the seeing conditions, although an important part of the flux received by the telescope may fall outside the slit, causing a considerable loss of light. So that the purity of the spectra will not suffer, we can construct an asymmetric spectrograph, in which the focal length of the collimator F_1 is greater than that of the camera objective, F_2. Thus the monochromatic image of the slit is reduced, on the plate, in the ratio F_2/F_1. For example, if $F_1/F_2 = 5$, we obtain an image of 20 μ with a slit of 100 μ. At the focus of a telescope having a focal length of 5 or 10 m, the turbulence must reach 1″ or 2″ for the loss of light to become sensible.

In the observation of extended sources, turbulence does not cause a loss of light. Its only effect is to cast onto the slit light from different portions of the source. In some cases this can hinder the observations of well defined regions in an extended source (planetary surfaces, condensations in spirals, etc.).

WIDENING OF STELLAR SPECTRA.—In the absence of atmospheric disturbances and with perfect guiding, the stellar spectra photographed with an objective prism or a slit spectrograph will have practically no width perpendicular to the dispersion (some hundredths of a millimeter). On such threadlike spectrograms the lines are scarcely visible and all microphotometric study is impractical.

To enlarge the spectra to some tenths of a millimeter during an exposure, we can slightly adjust the rate of the equatorial drive so that the motion is not exactly diurnal. If the apex of the prism (or lines of the grating) are placed parallel to the motion of the hour angle, the stellar image will be slowly displaced on the plate (or along the slit) perpendicular to the dispersion.

There is, however, a serious drawback to this procedure for a slit spectrograph, especially if the star is far from the zenith. Atmospheric refraction produces a small vertical spectrum at the focus of the telescope, since short wavelengths are raised higher above the horizon than long ones. When one guides on the visible image, the ultraviolet region can fall outside the slit. It is therefore better to rotate the spectrograph assembly around the optical axis of the collimator in such a way as to place the slit vertically, and to enlarge the spectrum mechanically by means of a plane parallel plate positioned in front of the slit and oscillating around a horizontal axis.

An equivalent solution consists of oscillating the plate holder around a mean position in its plane either in an alternating movement of translation or in a movement of rotation about an axis perpendicular to its plane and intersecting it somewhere along the projected continuation of the spectrum. In the latter case the widening is least pronounced at the end of the spectrum closest to the axis of rotation. Chalonge has exploited this effect in his prism spectrographs (§ 48) in order to comparatively strengthen the ultraviolet, which is more spread out by the dispersion and more absorbed by the atmosphere.

Finally, the widening has sometimes been accomplished by astigmatism (for example, by introducing a cylindrical lens), thereby substituting a short line for the point image of a star.

25. Measurement of wavelengths. Radial velocities.

Only slit spectrographs allow the accurate juxtaposition of spectra from a star and from a laboratory comparison source without any wavelength shift between them. For this effect, we illuminate the slit on each side of the star image with a source emitting a line spectrum of well-known wavelengths (a spark between iron electrodes, a tube of helium, of neon, etc.). By measuring the position of the stellar lines with respect to those of the reference spectrum, either with a microscope or recording microphotometer, we can easily evaluate their wavelengths. In a prismatic spectrum, a hyperbolic interpolation formula of the type

$$\lambda = \lambda_0 + \frac{c}{x - x_0},$$

generally suffices for calculating the wavelengths within a restricted spectral interval (where x is the abscissa corresponding to the wavelength λ). The wavelengths and abscissas of three reference spectrum lines allow the determination of the three constants c, x_0 and λ_0. Gratings present the advantage of giving an almost linear dispersion, without compressing together the long wavelengths. This dispersion can be represented by a parabolic formula

$$\lambda = \lambda_0 + ax + bx^2$$

where the constant b is small with respect to a.

These measurements lead to the identification of the lines present in stellar atmospheres. In general, the stellar lines show a certain shift $\Delta\lambda$ with respect to lines of the same element observed in the laboratory. This most often arises from the relative velocity of the star with respect to the observer, and increases proportionally to the wavelength. The *radial velocity* v_r (the projection of the relative velocity onto the radial line-of-sight) is deduced by applying the Doppler-Fizeau principle. Representing by c the velocity of light in a vacuum, we have

$$\frac{\Delta\lambda}{\lambda} = \frac{v_r}{c}.$$

A displacement of the stellar lines toward the red $(\Delta\lambda > 0)$ corresponds to a velocity of recession; a displacement toward the violet $(\Delta\lambda < 0)$ to a velocity of approach.

In order to compare the radial velocities of different stars, or of the same star at different epochs, it is convenient to reduce them to their *heliocentric* values (radial velocity with respect to the sun). The principal correction arises from the orbital movement of the earth around the sun (a speed of about 30 km/sec); the correction due to the rotation of the earth on its axis is much smaller.

The heliocentric radial velocities of most stars are of the order of kilometers or tens of kilometers per second; some exceed 100 km/sec. A velocity of 30 km/sec produces a relative displacement $\Delta\lambda/\lambda$ of about 10^{-4}. For $\lambda = 4000$ A, $\Delta\lambda$ equals 0.4 A. With a linear dispersion of 40 A/mm the displacement on the plate is then 10 μ. We can measure to nearly ± 2 μ if the line is very sharp, so that the relative error is 20%, and the radial velocity can be evaluated to about ± 6 km/sec. With a dispersion 10 times greater (4 A/mm), v_r can be determined to nearly ± 0.6 km/sec. But, in many stars, the precision is not limited by the dispersion, but by the width of the spectrum lines.

With slitless spectrographs it is impossible to juxtapose accurately a stellar spectrum and one from an artificial source, therefore making it impossible to measure the wavelengths of the lines in comparison to standard lines. Astronomers tried unsuccessfully for a long time to measure radial velocities with an objective prism, the only instrument capable of rapidly furnishing the spectra of a great number of faint stars. The problem was finally resolved about ten years ago by using an objective prism with a normal field (§ 23), following a method of inversion recommended earlier by Schwarzschild (Fehrenbach). It consists of juxtaposing on the plate two photographs of the same field, with the prism turned 180° on its optical axis between exposures. The comparison of the two spectra whose dispersions are inverted with respect to each other allows an evaluation of the radial velocity; however, one must know in advance the radial velocities of some stars in the field, measured by the classical methods with a slit spectrograph. A normal-field objective prism 40 cm in diameter permits photographing spectra of 12th-photographic magnitude stars in about an hour.

26. Photoelectric spectrophotometry

Instead of recording the various spectral radiations *simultaneously* on a photographic plate, we can receive them *successively* on a photoelectric cell. We then use a monochromator whose exit slit isolates a narrow spectral band, and we explore the spectrum either by rotating the dispersing system or by moving the exit slit.

The use of a photoelectric spectrometer eliminates the inevitable standardization of photographic photometry, and leads more directly to the measurement of intensities. It has particular interest in the study of infrared spectra where plates are unusable or lose their sensitivity. Thus Kuiper has studied the spectra of planets and some bright stars up to 2.5 μ by means of a lead sulfide cell. The spectrum of the night sky (emitted by the upper atmosphere) has been explored in the same manner up to 1.4 μ with a Cs–O–Ag photomultiplier (M. Dufay) and up to more than 2 μ with a Pb–S cell (Vallance Jones and Gush).

The successive recording of radiation can, however, constitute a serious inconvenience when its intensity is susceptible to rapid variations. Although Liller (1957) has obtained good recordings of stellar spectra by this method, we must worry that variations in transparency and atmospheric turbulence may sometimes distort the measurements. Many arrangements have been envisioned for eliminating this cause of errors. In the apparatus constructed by Guérin and Laffineur (1954), for example, one Cs–Sb photomultiplier receives successively the radiations isolated by the exit slit of a prism monochromator, while another identical multiplier continually receives the total radiation reflected from the prism's entrance face. The two photoelectric currents are sent, after amplification, into the two branches of a ratiometer, a device which measures the *ratio* of their intensities. Variations that affect all radiation equally (*neutral* absorption and turbulence) are thus eliminated. In point of fact, the deviations of light rays are not necessarily the same at each instant for all wavelengths (chromatic scintillation), but the most important fluctuations are very rapid (pseudo-periods in the order of 0.1 to 0.2 sec) and are not recorded by the ratiometer, whose period is 2 sec. Only the slower fluctuations can remain.

IMAGE BRIGHTNESS.—In the case of a point source having a line or continuous spectrum, the flux falling on the cathode is equal, with a little loss, to the flux collected by the projection of the objective and entering the collimator. The expressions (24.1) and (24.3) thus remain valid, except that in the latter, dl now represents the width of the monochromator's exit slit.

In the case of an extended source, the flux received by the cathode is obtained by multiplying the surface of the exit slit (height h, width $\mathrm{d}l$) by the intensity at its plane (formulas (24.4) and (24.5)). We thus get for a line spectrum, with the notation of § 24:

$$\mathscr{F} = T \cdot B \cdot \omega \cdot h \cdot \mathrm{d}l \simeq \frac{\pi}{4}\, T \cdot B \cdot \frac{h \cdot \mathrm{d}l}{n^2};$$

for a continuous spectrum,

$$\mathscr{F} = T \cdot b(\lambda) \cdot \frac{h \cdot \mathrm{d}l^2}{\delta} \simeq \frac{\pi}{4}\, T \cdot b(\lambda)\, \frac{h \cdot \mathrm{d}l^2}{\delta \cdot n^2}$$

(n is the focal ratio of the objective preceding the exit slit).

27. Electronic spectrograph

In the *electronic camera* of Lallemand, represented schematically in Figure 16, the photons striking the semi-transparent cathode release electrons, which, accelerated in an electric field having a potential difference of about 30 kV, are focused on a photographic plate. The

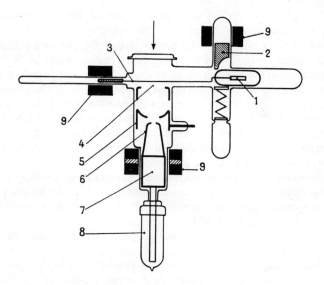

FIG. 16. LALLEMAND'S ELECTRONIC CAMERA.
1, the cathode in its vacuum tube; 2, hammer for breaking the tube; 3, arrangement for positioning the cathode; 4, holder for the cathode; 5, electrostatic lens; 6, anode; 7, plate magazine; 8, liquid air refrigerator; 9, magnetic controls.

electrons then form on the plate a copy of the image produced by the photons on the cathode.

After introducing the photocathode (contained in an evacuated glass tube) and the magazine of plates, an excellent vacuum is produced in the apparatus. A simple device controlled magnetically from the outside allows the tube containing the photocathode to be broken after the vacuum has been achieved. It allows a secure placement of the photocathode, and the substitution of one plate for another after each exposure. When all the plates have been exposed, the apparatus is opened so that the plates can be removed and developed. The photocathode, destroyed by contact with the air, must then be replaced.

This delicate technique achieves a considerable advantage over an ordinary photograph. The caesium–antimony cathode possesses a high quantum efficiency (§ 15). Moreover, on the most sensitive plate a great many photons are required to produce a developable grain of silver bromide, but each electron gives, after development, a track formed of 5 to 10 silver grains of small dimensions in the emulsion of the *nuclear track* plates (made for recording cosmic ray particles).

For application to the astronomical spectrograph, we arrange the photocathode in the focal plane of the spectrograph, which is placed at the end of a telescope. In normal situations, to give a sufficiently high density to the images, the necessary exposure can be 50 to 100 times shorter than for direct photography on a very sensitive plate, using the same spectrograph on the same telescope. Thus exposures of several minutes on the spectrum of the Orion nebula show as many faint emission lines as an ordinary photograph exposed many hours. In the case of a star, where only the total flux received by the telescope matters (§ 24), it is equivalent to multiplying the diameter of the mirror by a factor of about 7 to 10.

Electronic photography leads furthermore to a notable improvement in the resolution. The resolution is not limited by the aberrations of the electronic optics, but by the graininess of the nuclear track plate, which is finer than that of the usual emulsions. Finally, the blackening of the nuclear track plate receiving rapid electrons obeys a much simpler law than the blackening of plates exposed to photons: the optical density of a surface element is proportional to the number of electrons received. The photometric measurements are, in this case, greatly facilitated.

At the present time it is difficult to make an exposure longer than one hour, because the vacuum in the apparatus is as yet insufficient.

After an hour a fog appears on the plate due to the presence of ions. On the other hand, the camera can function for several dozen hours without sensible loss of advantage by changing the plates.

A very weak flux can be detected by counting with a microscope the characteristic electron tracks in the sensitive emulsion. This method, when applicable, can reach an advantage of 10,000 over an ordinary photograph.

Comparable to the electronic camera are the *image converters* used by Krassovsky and his colleagues for infrared spectrography of the night sky and the aurora as well as for astronomical photography. The infrared image received by the Cs–O–Ag photocathode is converted into an electronic image on a very fine (25 μ) fluorescent screen that forms the exit wall of the tube. Against this surface is applied the gelatine of the photographic plate to be exposed. The difference between the image converter and the Lallemand camera is essentially that in the image converter the plate is not exposed by electrons but by the photons emitted from the fluorescent substance. The result is naturally quite inferior, but the use of this apparatus is very convenient for long exposures since the vacuum can be maintained indefinitely and the cathode scarcely deteriorates.

CHAPTER IV

DESCRIPTION AND INITIAL
CLASSIFICATION OF STELLAR SPECTRA

I. PRINCIPAL ATOMIC AND MOLECULAR SPECTRA CHARACTERISTIC OF STELLAR ATMOSPHERES

28. General introduction to stellar spectra and their classification

Nearly all stars, including the sun, give a continuous spectrum crossed by absorption lines; some also show bright lines against the continuous background, accompanied by dark lines.

Since the beginning of its application to astrophysics, qualitative spectrum analysis has succeeded in identifying in stellar spectra a great number of lines that had been produced in the laboratory, and the conclusion was quickly reached that essentially the same atoms were being found in the atmospheres of stars as on the earth. With the present-day knowledge of atomic structure, this is trivial and self-evident. Yet only a century ago it was a surprise, and this discovery —the unity of the composition of the universe—was one of the first conquests of astrophysics.

One star varies greatly from another in the nature and intensity of its lines, as does the energy distribution in the continuum. By noting the common characteristics of different spectra as well as those which distinguish one from another, astronomers were quickly led to arrange the stars into a certain number of groups and subgroups formed of analogous objects, just as naturalists classify animals and plants into families, genera and species. Just as the ideal of the morphologist is to establish a "natural" classification with respect to the evolution of species, so the ideal classification of stellar spectra should lead to the formation of "natural groups" in relation to the probable evolution of stars, or, at the very least, groups arranged according to the conditions that prevail in their atmospheres: temperature, gravity and chemical composition.

Since most of the classifications rest essentially on the nature and intensity of lines present in the stellar spectra, it is useful to give first some idea of the atomic lines and molecular bands that play the chief roles in the classifications.

29. The hydrogen spectrum

The *wave numbers* of the lines (reciprocal of the wavelength in a vacuum) for atoms with a single planetary electron are given by the general formula

$$\sigma = RZ^2\left(\frac{1}{m_0^2} - \frac{1}{m^2}\right), \tag{29.1}$$

where Z is the atomic number, R the Rydberg constant

$$R = 2\pi\mu e^4/ch^3,$$

with e = the charge of the electron, c = the velocity of light in a vacuum, h = Planck's constant (see the numerical values in Table X at the end of the book). The *reduced mass* of the atom, μ, is $Mm_e/(M + m_e)$, M being the mass of the nucleus, m_e that of the electron.

For hydrogen, $Z = 1$, $R = 109{,}677.58$ kaysers (or cm^{-1}).

A line is emitted when an atom passes from an energy level represented by the *principal quantum number* m to a level characterized by the number $m_0 < m$ (m and m_0 being integers). It is absorbed when the atom passes from level m_0 to level $m > m_0$ [23].

As m increases in a *series* characterized by a given value of m_0, the lines approach one another, and when m approaches infinity, the wave number σ approaches the limit

$$\sigma_0 = RZ^2/m_0^2. \tag{29.2}$$

The *Lyman series* corresponds to $m_0 = 1$; this series falls completely in the far ultraviolet; the first lines have the following wavelengths (in air at 15° C at standard pressure):

$$m = 2, \quad \lambda = 1215.7 \text{ A } (L\alpha), \quad m = 3, \quad \lambda = 1025.8 \text{ A } (L\beta),$$

$$m = 4, \quad \lambda = 972.5 \text{ A } (L\gamma), \quad m = \infty, \quad \lambda_0 = 912 \text{ A (limit)}.$$

Although unobservable through the terrestrial atmosphere, the series nevertheless plays a most important role in astrophysics. From an altitude of 200 km, a spectrograph carried in a rocket has photographed the first 11 lines of the Lyman series in emission from the solar chromosphere (except for $L\gamma$, which is strongly absorbed by oxygen) and, up to 850 A, the continuous spectrum which extends it.

With $m_0 = 2$ we obtain the *Balmer series* in the visible and near ultraviolet. The wavelengths of the first lines and its limit are given in the left part of Table II. Intense in absorption in numerous stellar spectra (less however than the Lyman lines), the Balmer lines play a leading role in classification. We also observe them in emission in certain stars, in gaseous nebulae and in the solar chromosphere.

The *Paschen-Ritz series* $(m_0 = 3)$ is found in a region still easily accessible in the near infrared, with the following first lines and limit:

$$m = 4, \quad \lambda = 18751 \text{ A } (P\alpha), \quad m = 5, \quad \lambda = 12818 \text{ A } (P\beta),$$

$$m = 6, \quad \lambda = 10938 \text{ A } (P\gamma), \quad m = \infty, \quad \lambda_0 = 8204 \text{ A (limit)}.$$

It appears, but with less intensity, in stars which show the Balmer lines.

Still farther in the infrared we encounter the *Brackett series* $(m_0 = 4)$, with its first lines at 4.05 μ and 2.63 μ.

CONTINUOUS SPECTRA.—The absorption of radiation of wave number σ_0 (27.2) corresponds, in Bohr's model, to the transition of an electron to an orbit of infinite radius, that is to say, to the ionization of an atom. The energy of the absorbed photon is $h\nu_0$, where h represents Planck's constant and ν_0 is the frequency limit $c\sigma_0$.

Experiment shows that the atoms also absorb photons of frequency higher than ν_0. The energy absorbed is then higher than the ionization energy $h\nu_0$, and the extra amount appears in the form of kinetic energy communicated to the electron. The electron is expelled with a velocity v, which, in order to satisfy the principle of conservation of energy, must be such that

$$h\nu = h\nu_0 + \tfrac{1}{2}m_e v^2.$$

Conversely, when a proton captures an electron of speed v into an orbit of order m_0, a photon is emitted whose frequency is given by the preceding equation. Since the speed v can vary continuously, the same is true for the frequency ν.

Each of the hydrogen line series is thus extended toward the short wavelengths by a continuous spectrum, observable in absorption on account of ionizations in many stars, and observable in emission on account of recombinations of protons and electrons in certain very hot stars, gaseous nebulae, and the solar chromosphere. Of course, we actually observe only a finite number of lines in each series, variable according to the electron pressure. In an ionized gas, the electric field produced by the ions and electrons in the neighborhood of an atom perturb the outer orbits, which are no longer quantized (atomic

Stark effect). The series limit recedes toward the long wavelengths as the electron pressure becomes greater.

30. The spectrum of helium

IONIZED HELIUM.—The wave numbers of lines from the ion He$^+$, which possesses only a single planetary electron, are given by the formula (29.1), where $Z = 2$. When we take into account the reduced mass of the helium atom, R takes the value $R = 109{,}722.26$ k, a little larger than for hydrogen.

The series $m_0 = 1$ and $m_0 = 2$, in the far ultraviolet, cannot be observed through the terrestrial atmosphere, but the first line of the series $m_0 = 2$ has been recorded in the emission spectrum of the solar chromosphere ($\lambda = 1650.5$ A) from rockets at 115 km altitude.

In the *Fowler series* ($m_0 = 3$), only the first two lines are observable through the atmosphere, at 4685.7 and 3203.1 A. They are strong in many of the hot stars.

For $m_0 = 4$ (the *Pickering series*), formula (29.1) can be written

$$\sigma = 4R_{He}\left(\frac{1}{4^2} - \frac{1}{m^2}\right) = R_{He}\left[\frac{1}{2^2} - \frac{1}{(m/2)^2}\right].$$

If the constants R_{He} and R_H had exactly the same value, the lines of the Pickering series corresponding to even values of m would coincide precisely with the Balmer lines. Their wavelengths, being slightly different, are given in the right part of Table II. For a long time they were confused with the Balmer lines, since it is difficult to separate them. The lines corresponding to odd m values, observed by Pickering in the spectrum of ζ Pup were originally attributed to hydrogen. The Bohr theory showed that they belong to He$^+$.

NEUTRAL HELIUM.—Neutral helium, with two planetary electrons, already gives a much more complicated spectrum. Its most intense lines in the visible region (notably 5876 A) were discovered in emission in the solar chromosphere (1868), well before the gas was isolated on earth (1895).

The lines can be classed into two groups: those of triplets, of which two very close components are often inseparable, and those of singlets.

Each group contains 3 series of lines. Here are the wavelengths for the first lines of each series (for the triplets only the wavelength for the strongest double component is given):

Triplets

Principal series:	10830.3, 3888.6, 3187.7, ...
First secondary series:	5875.6, 4471.5, 4026.2, ...
Second secondary series:	7065.2, 4713.1, 4120.8, 3867.5, ...

Singlets
Principal series: 5015.7, 3964.7, 3613.6, ...
First secondary series: 6678.1, 4921.9, 4387.9, 4143.8, 4009.3
Second secondary series: 7281.3, 5047.7, 4437.5, 4169.0, 4024.0

Helium is, after hydrogen, the most abundant element in stellar atmospheres. The lines of neutral as well as those of ionized helium enter into the classification of hot stars.

TABLE II

THE BALMER SERIES OF HYDROGEN
AND THE PICKERING SERIES OF He$^+$

H, $m_0 = 2$			He$^+$, $m_0 = 4$			
m	λ		m	λ	m	λ
					5	10123.64
3	6562.82	Hα	6	6560.10	7	5411.52
4	4861.33	Hβ	8	4859.32	9	4541.59
5	4340.47	Hγ	10	4338.67	11	4199.83
6	4101.74	Hδ	12	4100.04	13	4025.60
7	3970.07	Hϵ	14	3968.43	15	3923.48
8	3889.05	Hζ	16	3887.44	17	3858.07
9	3835.39	H$_9$	18	3833.80	19	3813.50
10	3797.90	H$_{10}$	20	3796.33	21	3781.68
11	3770.63	H$_{11}$	..	....	..	....
12	3750.15	H$_{12}$				
13	3734.37	H$_{13}$				
....			..	....	..	....
∞	3645.98	(limit)	∞	3644.47	(limit)	

31. Lines of the nonmetals and metals

The majority of strong lines from neutral oxygen and nitrogen are found in the near infrared. The oxygen O I[1] spectrum is especially characterized by the lines 7775.4–7774.2–7772.0 and 8446.8–8446.3, which appear in the spectra of numerous stars, often with comparable intensities.

[1] In order to designate the spectrum of a neutral atom, we place after the symbol of the element the Roman numeral I (first spectrum); for atoms once or twice ionized, we use the numerals II, III (second and third spectra), etc. Thus He I represents the spectrum of neutral helium, He II that of the ion He$^+$, whereas O I, O II and O III correspond respectively to the atom O, and to the ions O$^+$ and O^{++}.

Singly or multiply ionized metalloids are found in hot stars. O II gives a complex spectrum, with the characteristic groups 4075.9–4072.2–4069.9, 4649.1–4641.8, 4319.6–4317.1, the lines 4414.9, 3973.3, 3749.5, etc. O III gives the strong line 3759.9. Ionized nitrogen N II also presents a very rich spectrum, with the lines 5679.6, 5666.6, 5005.1, 4447.0, 3995.0 and the easily recognized group 4630.5–4621.4–4613.9–4607.2–4601.5. N III is disclosed by the lines 4103.4, 4097.3, 4640.6, 4634.2 and 4379.1.

Carbon in its first stage of ionization is characterized by the doublet 4267.3–4267.0 (rarely resolved), when twice ionized by the triplet 4647.4–4650.2–4651.3, when three times ionized (C IV) by the doublet 5801.5–5812.1 and the strong line 4658.6.

Neutral silicon gives, along with numerous lines in the infrared, the lines 3905.5 and 4102.9; Si II has the lines 3856.0 and 3862.6, and the doublets 4130.9–4128.1, 5041.1–5056.0, 6347.1–6371.4.

Among the metallic lines we can scarcely even mention here any but those of the alkali metals, the alkali-earths, and magnesium. The D_1-D_2 doublet of neutral sodium (5895.9–5890.0) is well known in the solar spectrum. The relative intensity of the lines of neutral and ionized calcium plays an important role in spectral classification. Ca I is especially characterized by the resonance line 4226.7 (line g of the solar spectrum), Ca II by the first two lines of the principal series, which form the H and K doublet in the solar spectrum (3968.5–3933.7) and, in the infrared, by the lines 8662.1, 8542.1, 8498.0, which have the same upper energy level as H and K. The doublet corresponding to H and K in the spectrum of ionized strontium (Sr II) is 4215.5–4077.7, whereas the line 4607.3 is the most characteristic of the neutral atom.

The line 4481.3 of ionized magnesium (Mg II) is another of the most important in classification. Neutral magnesium is recognized by means of the triplet 5183.6–5172.7–5167.3, strong in the solar spectrum (lines b_4, b_2 and b_1).

The lines of the heavier metals in the neutral state (Fe I, Ti I, Cr I, Ni I, Sc I, etc.), so abundant in the solar spectrum, are much too numerous to cite here. The same atoms ionized are found in the spectra of hotter stars; they are preponderant in emission and in absorption in novae at a certain stage in their evolution. For instance, Fe II gives the strong lines 5316.6, 5169.0, 5018.4, 4923.9, 4583.8, 4549.5, 4351.8, 4233.2 .... The numerous lines of the twice-ionized Fe III have been found in the spectra of stars with a quite high temperature.

32. Molecular spectra

Molecular bands enter into the classification of low-temperature stars. The most important from this point of view are the bands shaded to the red, of titanium oxide TiO, which characterize one class of red stars. The bands of zirconium oxide ZrO, also shaded to red, accompany the bands of LaO in other stars.

Another class exhibits bands, shaded to the violet, of the carbon molecule C_2 (Swan spectrum). The first bands of the most important sequences have their heads at 4737, 5165 and 5635. The CN molecule also gives sequences of bands shaded to the violet, beginning at 3590, 3883, 4216 and 4606 A. The spectrum of CH, made up of complex bands having widely spaced lines, notably around 3900 and 4300 A, is found in many stars. The superposition of the 4300 band of CH and metallic lines forms the G band in the solar spectrum.

The existence of many other free radicals as well has been established in stellar atmospheres. Among those of diatomic composition we should cite MgH, SiH, AlH, ScO, VO, CrO, AlO, BO, SiF, SiN, identified in the spectrum of β Peg (Miss Davis, 1947). Finally, we find in the carbon stars the bands of C_3 and of SiC_2. (The bands of C_3 are also observed in emission in the spectra of comets, with those of C_2, CN and CH.) It is probable that triatomic or polyatomic molecules are also responsible for the continuous absorption observed in these same stars.

II. THE HARVARD CLASSIFICATION

33. Spectral classes and types: notation

The Harvard classification was gradually erected under the direction of Pickering, by Miss Maury, then by Miss Cannon and finally by Mrs. Mayall. It is associated with the *Henry Draper Catalogue*, which contains the spectra of more than 225,000 stars, with their photographic magnitudes. By adding the stars in the *Henry Draper Extension* and in various more restricted lists, and those which are shown on charts published with an indication of spectral type but without the magnitude, one obtains a total of more than 390,000 spectra classified at Harvard.

The spectra were photographed with glass objective prisms, giving a wide field but little dispersion, onto plates whose sensitivity did not extend above 5000 A. Thus the classification rests on the most salient characteristics visible under low dispersion between 3900 and 5000 A. With the additions and improvements that have been carried out successively at Mt. Wilson, Yerkes Observatory or by recommendation of the International Astronomical Union (taking into account the observations made in the visible region), the Harvard classification stands today as the foundation for the classification of stellar spectra. It depends on the presence or absence of key lines and on the relative strengths of the lines observed.

The stars are at present divided into 12 or 13 classes, each being designated in a purely arbitrary manner by one of the following capital letters:

$$Q, P, W, O, B, A, F, G, K, M, S, R, N;$$

the latter two can be united into the single class designated by C.

In principle each class is in turn divided into 10 groups, which we shall call *spectral types*; each type is designated by a digit $0, 1, 2, \ldots, 9$, placed after the capital letter for the class. But, in fact, not all of the subdivisions are used. In a general way there has been an endeavor to maintain a uniform gradation between successive types: for example, type B2 is approximately midway between types B1 and B3, type B9 between types B8 and A0.

The decimal subdivision does not apply to the classes whose spectra do not seem to form a continuous sequence (Q, P). We then distinguish the types by placing after the capital letter for the class a small letter a, b, c, d .... Formerly this applied also to classes O and M, for which the decimal subdivision was not adopted until later, when the continuity of the different types became apparent.

In order to direct attention to some peculiarity of the spectrum, we can complete the symbol with a "prefix" or "suffix."

Prefixes.—In "c" spectra the majority of lines are remarkably fine and present a narrow profile. Example: α Cygni cA2 (see Fig. 17c). We shall see that these stars are supergiants (§ 38). The prefix "c" is not used for O stars, which are all very luminous. "g" stars are giants; "d" stars are dwarfs. Their spectral characteristics will be indicated later (§§ 36, 37).

Suffixes.—"n" designates wide and diffuse (nebulous) lines; "s" designates well defined lines with a narrow profile (sharp), without exhibiting the fineness noted by the characteristic "c." These suffixes serve in classes B and A.

"e" denotes the presence of emission lines in a class where they are not regularly expected. Thus it is not employed for classes Q, P and W. For O and B stars this generally means that the Balmer lines are in emission. We can then place after the "e" the Greek letter of the last Balmer line present in emission, starting with Hα.

"ev" designates variable emission lines.

"v" is for a variable spectrum.

"k" indicates the presence of interstellar absorption lines of Ca^+ (H and K).

"pec" signals the fact that the spectrum contains peculiarities that tend to remove it from the class to which it is attached. It can refer, for example, to the exceptional strength of certain lines (Si II 4131–4128 or Sr II 4215 in an A star).

"pq" indicates a spectral peculiarity similar to those of novae (class Q).

34. The essential characteristics of the different spectral classes

We shall not discuss class P, reserved for gaseous nebulae, nor class Q, peculiar to novae. Neither of these is attached directly to the other spectral classes, for which we shall give here the essential characteristics. A more detailed description of the different types will be found in the following chapter, including the principal criteria used today for the subdivision of the classes.

The *Wolf-Rayet stars* (named for the two astronomers at Paris who discovered them in 1876), grouped into class W (the old Harvard types Oa, Ob and Oc) are distinguished from all the other stars by the presence of broad and intense emission lines, among which are found those of ionized helium (Fig. 24, § 40).

In the spectra of O stars (old Harvard types Od, Oe and Oe5), the lines of ionized helium, belonging mainly to the Pickering series, are still present, but this time in absorption.

They have practically disappeared in class B, whereas the lines of neutral helium continue alongside the generally stronger lines of hydrogen (Fig. 17a).

In their turn the lines of neutral helium fade away in class A, where the Balmer lines predominate, very strong and generally broad (Fig. 17b, c, 18a).

While the B and A stars are in general very white or even slightly tinged with blue, those of the classes following, F, G, K, appear to us in contrast more and more yellowish.

The spectra of F stars still very much resemble those of A stars. The Balmer lines are still very strong, but their intensity gradually diminishes. On the other hand, the strength of the metal lines increases, and the H and K lines of ionized calcium are quite obvious (Fig. 18b).

Class G includes yellow stars whose spectra resemble that of the sun.

The number and intensity of metal lines have so increased that the lines of hydrogen, although still rather strong, no longer attract immediate attention from among the lines. H and K are by far the most intense lines (Fig. 19a).

The yellow color is accentuated in the K class, because the continuous spectrum weakens rapidly toward the short wavelengths, while the metal lines become even stronger. The spectrum resembles

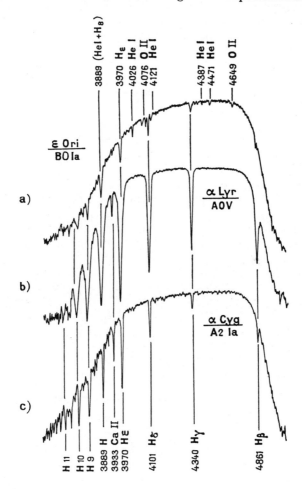

FIG. 17. MICROPHOTOMETER TRACINGS OF THE SPECTRA OF B0, A0 AND A2 STARS (taken by the author with the objective prism at the Observatory of Lyon).

that of sunspots; the lines H and K of Ca$^+$ are always very strong, but the resonance line of neutral calcium at 4227 A is now even more intense (Fig. 19*b*).

Starting with class M, molecular spectra play an essential role in the classification of the stars, which have become reddish. The M stars are characterized by absorption bands of titanium oxide (TiO) that are shaded to the red, giving the spectrum a peculiar fluted appearance (Fig. 19*c*).

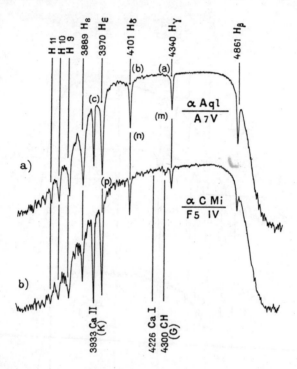

FIG. 18. MICROPHOTOMETER TRACINGS OF THE SPECTRA OF A7 AND F5 STARS.

On the other hand, the zirconium oxide bands (ZrO), also shaded to the red, dominate in those few stars grouped in class S. The ZrO bands were much weaker in M stars.

Finally, the R and N carbon stars, now united in a single class C, show instead of metallic oxide bands the bands of carbon (C_2) and cyanogen (CN), shaded to the violet.

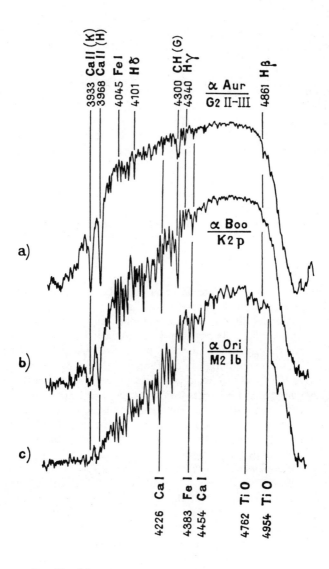

FIG. 19.   MICROPHOTOMETER TRACINGS OF THE SPECTRA
OF G2, K2 AND M2 STARS.

35. Spectral classification, excitation and temperature

If for the time being we set apart the W stars and red stars, the diversity of stellar spectra is caused essentially not by a difference of chemical composition, but by varying excitation conditions.

When the same element is found both in an ionized and a neutral state in the spectral series, we find first the ionized atom, then the neutral atom in going down the sequence from class O to class M. Thus the intensity of the He II absorption lines decreases beginning with type O5; that of the He I lines attains its maximum in B3. Similarly the lines of Ca II appear around type B5, grow progressively stronger up to K0 and then weaken; appearing much later, in class A, the resonance line 4227 A of Ca I continually grows in intensity down through class M.

Elements whose successive ionization energies are rather close, such as silicon, furnish still more impressive examples. The maximum intensity of the lines of silicon thrice, twice and once ionized and of neutral silicon is encountered in the following types:

$$\text{Si IV}:\text{O9}; \quad \text{Si III}:\text{B1}; \quad \text{Si II}:\text{A0}; \quad \text{Si I}:\text{G5}.$$

The diagram of Figure 20 was constructed by placing on the abscissa the spectral types corresponding to the maximum intensity of the characteristic lines of certain elements, and on the ordinate, the excitation energies. We see that the higher the excitation energy, the sooner the maximum intensity of the lines occurs in the spectral series. Thus, even though lines of much different excitation energies coexist in the same spectral type, we can conclude that the excitation energy constantly diminishes from class O to class M.

In the W stars, the bright lines ought to be emitted by the recombination of ions and electrons. The production of He II lines in absorption requires only the excitation of He^+ ions, but the emission of the same lines requires the previous ionization of the He^+ ions. *Thus the excitation diminishes from class W to class M.*

The temperature is one of the essential factors which govern the ionization and excitation of the atoms. Now, a simple qualitative examination shows that the maximum energy in the continuous spectrum is progressively displaced from the ultraviolet in class O toward the infrared in class M (bluish white stars, yellowish white, then yellow and red). Even before studying the color temperatures of stars (Chap. VI), we can be assured that the temperature diminishes from the O stars to the M stars.

By the distribution of energy in their continuous spectra, the stars of the first C (or R0) types are joined to class G, whereas the M and S stars are joined to class K, conforming to the scheme

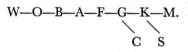

To summarize: the Harvard classification, in its revised and completed form, has thus succeeded in classifying the stars in the order of decreasing temperature. *It is a one-parameter classification, and that parameter is associated with the temperature of the layers of the stellar atmosphere where the lines are produced.*

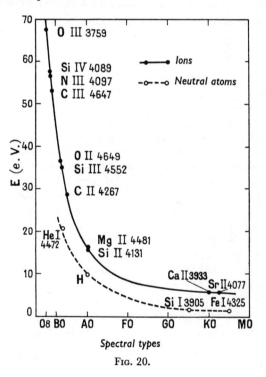

Fig. 20.

CHAPTER V

SPECTRA AND ABSOLUTE MAGNITUDES

I. SPECTROSCOPIC CRITERIA OF ABSOLUTE MAGNITUDES

36. Absolute spectroscopic magnitudes of F to M stars

The first researches on the distribution of absolute magnitudes among the stars of different spectral types were based on the absolute magnitudes deduced from trigonometric parallaxes [10, 11, 25] or dynamic parallaxes of double stars (§ 67) (Hertzsprung, Russell, 1905–1914). They had shown, for F to M stars, the existence of two quite distinct groups: the *dwarf* stars of low luminous intensity, and the *giants*, of high luminosity.

Presumably stars as different as giants and dwarfs should have shown in their spectra certain distinctive characteristics. This problem was attacked and resolved by Adams and Kohlschütter in 1914.

Let us consider two stars of the same spectral type and similar apparent brightness. One has a small proper motion, the other a much greater proper motion [8, 11]. There is a high probability that the first will be much more distant, and therefore much more luminous than the second. By forming a series of star pairs in this manner and by carefully examining their spectra, Adams and Kohlschütter discovered that certain metal lines are strong in stars of high luminosity, weak in stars of low luminosity. An opposite effect is observed for other spectral lines.

Thus, for stars of high luminosity, the lines

Sr II 4077 and 4215, Ti II 4161 and 4399, Fe II 4233A

are particularly intense, whereas the following lines are especially weak:

Cr I 4324, Ca I 4435 and 4454, Ti I 4535 A.

The first are lines of ionized atoms, the second lines of neutral atoms. Among the lines "sensitive to absolute magnitude," it is thus well to distinguish the lines of ionized atoms, stronger in the very luminous stars, from those of neutral atoms, relatively weak in these same stars.

Adams and Kohlschütter have also noted that the continuous spectra of giants weaken more rapidly on the short wavelength side than those of dwarfs. The effect is more noticeable in class K than in class F or in early G types. Since the proper motions (and undoubtedly the distances) are more nearly the same for the K star pairs than for the G pairs, the weakening toward the violet cannot be entirely attributed to interstellar absorption. Its origin must be sought, at least in part, in the atmospheres of the stars themselves.

The high luminosity M stars show abnormally strong Balmer lines. The fact that the radial velocity measured from the hydrogen lines is the same as for the other lines suffices to prove that this also must be a phenomenon belonging to the atmospheres of these stars.

The first discovery led at once to the spectroscopic determination of absolute magnitudes. For a certain number of stars belonging to a given spectral type, we know the parallax measured by the trigonometric method or an indirect method. In their spectra we evaluate the ratio of intensities of two neighboring lines of which one is sensitive to the absolute magnitude, and we construct a graph with the intensity ratio of the two lines versus the absolute magnitudes. The points will fall on a regular curve, often nearly a straight line, which serves to determine the absolute magnitudes of stars of the same spectral type but of unknown parallax, after the intensity ratio of the lines has been evaluated in their spectra. This can be "estimated" visually, without any photometric measurements.

By thus proceeding entirely empirically, Adams and Joy obtained rather rapidly the absolute magnitudes of a great number of stars in classes F to M (a list of 1600 stars was published in 1932, of 4179 stars in 1935). The method has been applied by other observatories, often with different luminosity criteria, since these are tied to the dispersion of the spectrograms.

Lindblad has discovered another very important criterion, applicable to spectra taken with an objective prism of low dispersion. The violet CN bands are much stronger in the G and K giants than in the dwarfs of the same type.[1] The Swedish astronomers measured by a correct photometric method the monochromatic magnitude difference on each side of the CN 4216 band head (at 4260 and 4180 A). The 4300 band of CH shows an analogous but much less pronounced effect.

37. Extension to A and B stars

It was necessary to find other luminosity criteria in order to extend the spectroscopic determination of absolute magnitudes to stars of the

[1] With the exception of the population II giants (§ 38), where the CN bands are weak.

early spectral classes where metallic lines are very weak or absent. An additional difficulty was presented by the B stars, which are in general too distant for their parallaxes to be accessible by a direct measurement.   One thus had available only a few absolute magnitudes sure enough for tracing the standardization curves.

Abetti has shown that in the classes A and B, the appearance of the hydrogen lines depends on the luminosity.   The lines are relatively narrow and well-defined in the most luminous stars, much more diffuse in those less luminous.   Adams and Joy therefore attempted to determine the absolute magnitudes by distinguishing between "s" and "n" stars (§ 33) in each spectral type.   Later E. G. Williams formed three luminosity classes after determining exactly the spectral type from photographic spectrophotometric measurements of the total intensity of the lines of hydrogen, of He I, or also of Mg II and Si II (§ 45).   We will examine later the new criteria added by Morgan and Keenan (§ 39).

The classification developed at Stockholm and at Uppsala (Lindblad, Schalén, Öhman, Elvius, Westerlund, ...) rests essentially on the total intensity of the Hγ and Hδ lines, which gradually increases when the luminosity diminishes; the photometric measurements are made on low dispersion spectra.   The B and A0 stars are arranged in several classes of decreasing luminosity, arbitrarily designated by Greek letters (τ, τ^-, σ^+, σ, ρ, μ) [15].

The application of spectroscopic methods has brought about considerable progress in the knowledge of stellar distances.   The trigonometric parallax can be measured, under the best conditions, with an *absolute* error in the vicinity of 0".007.   The *relative* error in the distance $\Delta r/r = \Delta p/p$ thus increases proportionally to the distance.   Although it scarcely surpasses 7% for stars situated 10 pc from the sun, it already attains 35% at 50 pc, 70% at 100 pc, and the method is by then no longer applicable.   The distances deduced from the absolute spectroscopic magnitudes are never precise and can carry a *relative* error in the order of 20 or 25%.   But this error is *independent of distance*.

II. HERTZSPRUNG-RUSSELL DIAGRAMS AND SPECTRAL CLASSIFICATIONS WITH TWO PARAMETERS

38. Spectrum-luminosity and color-luminosity diagrams

The solid contribution of spectroscopic absolute magnitudes has served to enrich considerably the Hertzsprung-Russell (H-R) diagrams, drawn originally with the aid of absolute magnitudes deduced from trigonometric or dynamic parallaxes.

Let us place on the abscissa the stellar spectral type, considered as a rather well-defined variable; on the ordinate, the absolute visual magnitude. Rather than falling randomly on the graph, the points group along two distinct lines, corresponding to two great families of

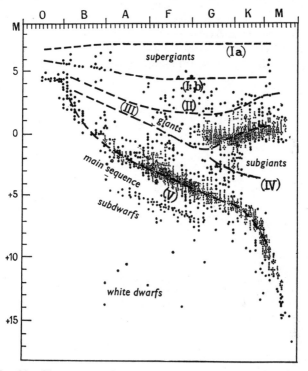

FIG. 21. HERTZSPRUNG-RUSSELL DIAGRAM (PARENAGO, 1953) AND THE LUMINOSITY CLASSES OF MORGAN AND KEENAN (according to PECKER).

stars: the one where the luminosity gradually diminishes from class B to class M, the other, where the luminosity is always great and varies little with spectral type. The first constitutes the *main sequence* or *dwarf branch*, the second the *giant branch* (Fig. 21).

The two families are quite widely separated in classes K and M. We recognize only very luminous M stars (around $M_v = -2$ to 0) and very weak M stars (around $M_v = 9$ or 10). The ratio of their intensities is at least 10,000.

We find also, in all the spectral classes, a small number of stars much more luminous still than the giants, whose absolute magnitude reaches $M_v = -6$ or -7, and which are called *supergiants*. One or two magnitudes below the main sequence the *subdwarfs* are sometimes encountered. Finally, very far below the main sequence, are found a few stars such as *o* Eridani B and Sirius B, with a very small luminous intensity ($M_v = +10$ to $+15$), especially between types B5 and F0. These are the *white dwarfs*, whose spectra show only the first Balmer lines, in absorption and considerably broadened.

Nowadays we very frequently construct the diagram with the color index on the abscissa, since it follows the spectral type exactly (§ 51)

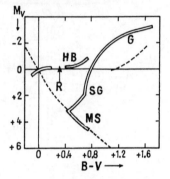

FIG. 22. SCHEMATIC COLOR-LUMINOSITY DIAGRAM OF THE
GLOBULAR CLUSTER M3 (from observations of SANDAGE).
MS, main sequence; SG, subgiants; G, giants; HB, horizontal branch; R, RR Lyrae variables. The dashes trace the main sequence and giant branch of population I.

and can be measured with precision by photoelectric photometry, for example, in the B–V sytems (§ 18).

Three important remarks on the subject of spectrum-luminosity or color-luminosity diagrams must be made immediately:

1. In their classical form (Fig. 21) they concern the majority of stars situated, like the sun, in the spiral arms of our galaxy or of other galaxies and belonging to Baade's *population I*. *Population II* includes the stars of globular clusters, of elliptical galaxies, of the nucleus region and halo of the Milky Way or of other spirals. It is essentially characterized by the absence of interstellar matter and of blue supergiants. Its spectrum-luminosity diagram is quite different but still poorly known, because its stars are necessarily distant and in general very faint. It has been possible, however, to trace the color-luminosity diagram of a certain number of globular clusters, in the form of a sidewise Y (Fig. 22). We do not find any white stars in the main

sequence, and the red giants are more luminous than those of population I. The following paragraphs will deal exclusively with population I, the better known of the two.

2. On H-R diagrams constructed with a great number of stars (almost all of population I), the dispersion of individual points around the principal branches is in general rather considerable. This arises in large part from the uncertainty in absolute magnitudes, since it is greatly reduced when only the stars in the vicinity of the sun are used, whose parallaxes are well known [11 (Fig. 4, p. 29)].

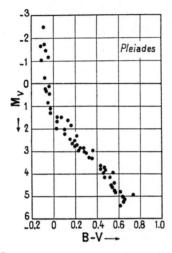

FIG. 23.   COLOR-LUMINOSITY DIAGRAM OF THE PLEIADES
(JOHNSON and MORGAN).

If we consider the stars belonging to the same galactic cluster, all situated at practically the same distance from the sun, the apparent magnitudes, determined with precision, differ only by a constant from the absolute magnitudes, provided that the interstellar absorption is the same in front of all the stars of the cluster. We then find that the dispersion of points along the main sequence is extremely small. By way of example, Figure 23 shows the color-luminosity diagram for the Pleiades. However, the line forming the upper part of the main sequence (in the direction of the blue stars) differs from one cluster to another (Fig. 51, § 78) and, when the cluster contains giants (they are always rare), their position on the diagram is still more variable. When one takes at random a great number of stars from our galaxy, it is possible for the line to be less well defined toward the blue end of

the main sequence and especially in the giant region.   The group
can also contain some samples of population II (high velocity stars).
A certain dispersion of points will result, certainly real this time.

3. The distribution of points on the general diagrams gives no idea
of the true proportion of members of each family; only the diagrams
of clusters can be considered as significant in this regard.

In effect we have determined the absolute magnitudes for only a
very small number of stars in the Galaxy: Let us suppose, for
example, that the absolute magnitudes of all the bright stars, up to
the 5th apparent magnitude, are known, numbering about 1500 (we
also know those of a certain number of fainter stars).   The most
distant of the 5th magnitude stars are found a thousand parsecs from
the sun.   Now the total number of stars contained within a sphere
of 1000 pc radius around the sun would be in the order of 30 million.
We cannot hope to know the properties of the group by means of this
sample in the proportion of 1/20,000 (Lundmark).   Furthermore, the
sample is completely falsified by a selection effect: we observe relatively
many giants and supergiants because they are visible from afar, but in
reality their number is very small.   Conversely, the proportion of
low luminosity stars, red stars of the main sequence and especially
white dwarfs ought to be much larger than indicated by the distribution
on the diagrams.

39. The Yerkes two-dimensional classification [16]

Since within one spectral type the absolute magnitudes group
themselves with rather little dispersion around well-defined values
corresponding to the various stellar families, we can limit ourselves to
arranging the stars in a small number of *luminosity classes* (§ 37),
instead of trying to determine the absolute magnitude of each one.
This has been the procedure of W. W. Morgan and P. C. Keenan,
with the collaboration of Miss E. Kellman, in erecting the two-
dimensional classification of the Yerkes Observatory (MKK system).
The first parameter is spectral type, which almost always coincides
with that of Harvard; the second is the luminosity class, indicated by
a Roman numeral following the symbol for the spectral type.   Note
the significance of the numerals used (Fig. 21): Ia—the most luminous
supergiants; Ib—less luminous supergiants; II—luminous giants;
III—normal giants; IV—subgiants; V—main sequence stars.

The absolute magnitudes of these various classes, which have been
determined for each spectral type, can be revised if necessary without
any modification taking place in the classification itself.

The subdwarfs and white dwarfs, attached to population II, have not been classified at Yerkes, nor stars earlier than O9, nor, at the other end of the classification, the very few stars of classes S and C.

The MKK classification of stars O9 to M2 is illustrated in the Yerkes *Atlas of Stellar Spectra* (1943), accompanied by a detailed commentary. The spectra have been photographed with a fairly low dispersion ($\simeq 125$ A/mm), allowing rather faint stars to be reached. When one works with an entirely different dispersion, it is generally necessary to modify the criteria of spectral type and luminosity, because the ratio of the intensities of insufficiently resolved lines varies with dispersion. Like the Harvard classification and the first determinations of absolute magnitude at Mount Wilson, the MKK classification rests uniquely on the visual examination of spectrograms and not on photometric measurements like those of the Swedish astronomers and of E. G. Williams.

Table III reviews some of the principal criteria of spectral type and luminosity utilized at Yerkes.

40. On the classification of hot stars

It is now convenient to complete the description of spectrum features for the stars not classified at Yerkes, given very briefly before (§ 34).

CLASS W.—The Wolf-Rayet stars, all very luminous but with rather uncertain absolute magnitudes, form two parallel series. In one, designated by the symbol WC, there dominate, besides the lines of He II, those of carbon and oxygen in various stages of ionization: C II, C III, C IV; O II, O III, O IV, O V and O VI. In the other, designated by WN, lines of nitrogen dominate: N III, N IV and N V. The lines of carbon and oxygen in the one kind, those of nitrogen in the other, seem to be almost mutually exclusive (Fig. 24).

In the WC sequence, the strongest emission lines are, in the blue, C III 4650 and He II 4686; in the visible region, C III 5696, C IV 5812, then He II 5411, O V 5470 and 5592, He I 5876. In the red and near infrared C IV 7726, C III 8255, 6744 are observed; C II 7236–7231 and He II 6560 (not separated from Hα).

Beals distinguished 3 types of decreasing excitation: WC 6, WC 7 and WC 8, according to the ratio of the intensities of C IV and C III. The width of the lines, which is of the order of 70 A in the type WC 6 (where C III 4650 cannot be separated from He II 4686), is only about 35 A in type WC 7 and a dozen angstroms in WC 8.

In the WN sequence, less rich in lines, 4686 is preponderant in the blue beside various lines of nitrogen, often joining in a single band

TABLE

MKK (YERKES)

	Criteria for spectral types
	Ratios of Si III/Si IV, Si II/Si III, Si II/He I
B0	4552 Si III/4089 Si IV (< 1)
B1	.........."......... (> 1)
B2–B3	4128–31 Si II/4121 He I. In B3 the K line appears.
B5	.... 4144 He I
B9	4481 Mg II ≫ 4471 He I
	Increasing intensity of metal lines
A0	He I very weak or absent; Fe II very weak
A1	4030–34 Mn I appears, 4385 (blend)/4481 Mg II
A2–A5	............/4128–31, 4300 (blend)/4385
F0	.................." ....
F2	*G* band shades off toward the red (CH)
F5	*G* band is intensified, 4045 Fe I/Hδ, 4226 Ca I/Hγ
G0	....................." ....
G5	4030–34/4300 violet side of *G*, 4325 Fe I/Hγ
K0	........"........, 4290 (blend)/4300, 4096/Hδ
K5	4226 Ca I/4325 Fe I, ..." ....
M0 to M5	*Increasing intensity of* TiO *bands* Band heads: 4762, 4954, 5168, 5445, 5763, 5816, 5857 (farther out 6651, 7054, 7589)

Blend = mixture of many lines of

III

CLASSIFICATION

Criteria for increasing luminosity	Type stars
4089 Si IV/4009 He I	B0 Ia ε Ori, V δ Sco
3995 N II/4009, 4552/4387 He I	B1 Iab ζ Per
............."	B2 III γ Ori, V ζ Cas; B3 V η UMa
Balmer lines sharper	B5 III δ Per
	B7 V α Leo; B8 Iab β Ori
............."	B9 III γ Lyr
............."	
(Fe II a little stronger)	A0 III α Dra, IV γ Gem, V α Lyr
	A1 V α CMa
4416 (blend)/4481, 4416/4300	A2 Ia α Cyg; A3 III β Tri
	A4 III α Oph; A5 V δ Cas
	A7 III γ Boo
............."	F0 Ib α Lep; V γ Vir
...."....and 4172/4226 Ca I	F2 IV β Cas
4077 Sr II/4226, 4045, 4063, 4250	
Fe I	F5 Ib γ Cyg, V β Vir
............."	G0 Ib α Aqr, II α Sag, IV η Boo
	G2 V the sun, 16 Cyg A
4077/4062 Fe I, 4085, 4144, 4250	
Fe I	G5 IV μ Her; G8 II ζ Cyg
CN *bands stronger* 4215–4144	G8 III δ Boo, IV β Aql, V ζ Boo A
4077/4063, 4077/4071	
CN *band* 4216	K0 III ε Cyg, IV η Cep; K1 IV γ Cep
	K2 Ib ε Peg, III α Ari, V ε Eri
....." ....., 4215 Sr II/4250	
Fe I	K3 Ib η Per, II γ Agl, III δ And
	K5 II ζ Cyg, III α Tau, V 61 Cyg A
Increasing intensity of H lines (§ 36)	M0 III β And
For giants and supergiants: decreasing intensity of 4226	M2 Ia μ Cep, Ib α Ori
Ca I. 4077 Sr II/4045 Fe I, 4215 Sr II/4250 Fe I	M5 II α Her

the same element or different elements.

around 4640.   The principal lines of the visible region are He II 5411, He I 5876 and, farther toward the red, He II 6560, He I 6678; N IV 7109.   The subdivision into types (from WN 5 to WN 8) also depends on the intensity ratios of different ions.

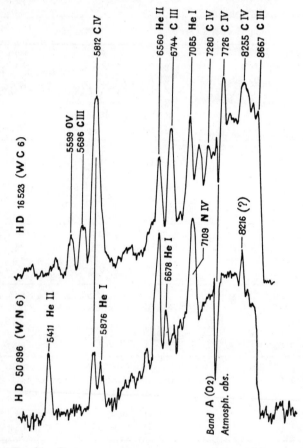

FIG. 24.   SPECTRA OF WR STARS IN THE RED AND NEAR INFRARED
(Y. ANDRILLAT, Haute Provence Observatory).

The ratio of intensities of the lines He II 5411 and He I 5876 follows a parallel course in the two series, WC 7 and WC 8 corresponding to WN 7 and WN 8 respectively.   The excitations thus appear comparable.

With the Wolf-Rayet stars are associated the *nuclei* of many planetary nebulae (population II). But in these latter, the lines are less wide and one observes the coexistence of carbon, oxygen and nitrogen.

CLASS O (classification of H. H. Plaskett, revised by Petrie).—All these stars are very luminous ($M_{pv} \simeq -5$). Certain ones still show in emission the line 4686 of the Fowler series (29 CMa), sometimes accompanied by N III 4640 (ζ Pup) or of Hα. But the lines of the Pickering series are in absorption, like those of He I, H, Si IV. The lines of N III, O III and C III are weak. Petrie distinguishes 5 types denoted by O5–O9, according to the intensity ratios of the lines of He II and He I, He II and H, He II and Si IV.

The lines of the Pickering series attain their maximum intensity around type O5. Those of He I increase in strength from O5 to O9, just as Si IV 4089 and 4116 do. It is around O7 that the N III lines are the strongest and C III 4650 begins to appear.

Type stars: O5 ζ Pup, O6 λ Cep, O7 S Mon, O8 λ Ori, O9 10 Lac.

BE STARS.—A rather large number of B stars show the lines of the Balmer series in emission, the first being the most frequent (Hα only, then Hα and Hβ, etc.). They are often double and sometimes accompanied by the emission lines of metallic ions (Fe II). Their profiles and intensities are almost always variable, sometimes very rapidly (Mme. R. Herman). When these stars exhibit in emission a rather large number of Balmer lines, they are redder than normal B stars of the same type, because the continuous emission spectrum, which extends the Paschen series (§ 29), reinforces the red region of the spectrum.

41. Peculiar stars of classes A and F [16]

With classes A and F are associated numerous stars that are difficult to classify on account of the anomalous intensity of certain lines. We distinguish:

1. *Magnesium, silicon and europium stars*, where the lines of one of these elements in an ionized state are particularly intense (Mn II, for example, in α And, B9p). Often we observe the simultaneous reinforcement of Eu II and Cr II, sometimes of Eu II, Cr II and Sr II, ... Study of the Zeeman effect often shows in these stars the existence of strong magnetic fields, varying periodically or in an irregular manner (H. W. Babcock).

2. *Metallic line stars* where certain metallic lines are abnormally strong whereas those of Ca II are weak. The intensity of the K line would place them in class A, that of the Balmer lines would assign them an early F type, while that of other metallic lines would suggest

a later F type. In 15 UMa, for example, one would obtain with these three criteria the types A2, F0 and F5; for τ UMa, A5, F0 and F6. The abundance of Na, Sr and Zn atoms appears larger than in normal stars, that of Ca and Sc smaller.

42. Red stars [16]

Me stars.—In class M belong many long-period variables, often of large amplitude, such as o Cet (*Mira Ceti*), spectrum M9e. They show the hydrogen lines *in emission* during a large part of their cycle of variation. But, contrary to what appears in Be stars, where the strength of the lines followed the order Hα, Hβ, etc., in this case Hα is relatively weak, Hβ almost invisible, Hγ and especially Hδ are strong, and Hϵ is practically nonexistent. The emission must be produced in a relatively deep layer of the stellar atmosphere, and the various Balmer lines each suffer a different weakening from the bands and absorption lines in the overlying layers. All the Me stars studied by Merrill and Joy show in emission the forbidden lines of Fe II in the vicinity of minimum light. In the spectrum of *Mira Ceti*, the bands of AlO are also seen in emission (Joy).

Class S.—We know of scarcely 70 S stars brighter than magnitude $m_v = 11.0$. They are giants of absolute magnitude $M_v \simeq -1$. The most apparent bands of ZrO are 5552, 5629, 5718 (β system). The other systems (α 4620, 4638, 4641; γ 6474) furnish less sensitive criteria. The bands of LaO, YO, SiH are also present, and those of TiO are weak. Keenan's classification (1954) depended on the LaO bands at 7403 and 7910, quite visible in the later types of S stars.

The lines of the relatively heavy atoms Sr I (4607), Ba II (4554), Y, Zr, Nb, La and the rare earths are much more intense than in the M stars. Also discovered in the S stars are the lines of neutral technetium (Tc I), a radioactive atom whose half-life is only a few million years.

The Se variables, like the Me variables, show the Balmer lines in emission. But they do not present the same anomalies in the distribution of intensities, which are explained by the different nature of the overlying molecular absorption.

Carbon stars.—The classification of Keenan and Morgan (1941), revised by Bouigue (1954), groups the R and N stars of the Harvard system into a single class, C. The decimal subdivision depends on:

1. The progressive weakening of the continuous spectrum toward the violet, measured in narrow spectral regions only lightly affected by the bands (6150, 5670, 5190 A);

2. The increasing intensity of the sodium D doublet, the lines generally strongest in the spectrum (in WC Cas the resonance doublet 6707 of lithium is extremely intense);

3. The intensity ratio of the bands of C_2 at 5635 and 5585, which increases as the temperature (of rotation) decreases.

Within the same type the intensity of the C_2 bands, quite variable from one star to another, is indicated by an index following the type symbol (examples: T Lyn = $C6_3$, U Cyg = $C9_2$).

Study of the C_2 and CN bands has revealed a very high abundance of the carbon isotope C^{13} ($C^{12}C^{13}$ and $C^{13}N^{14}$ molecules). The ratio of the numbers of the C^{13} and C^{12} atoms reaches 1/4 or 1/3 (McKellar), compared to 1/90 for terrestrial carbon and that of meteorites.

We also observe NH bands in the ultraviolet (Wildt). In the later C types the bands of C_3 appear (around 4050), and, in the green, those of SiC_2. With each of these triatomic molecules is associated a continuous spectrum in the violet and ultraviolet, which can be responsible for the weakening of the spectrum toward the short wavelengths. Some have also thought of attributing this continuous absorption to graphite dust (Swings and Rosen).

In the spectrum of 19 Psc ($C6_2$) Merrill has observed 4 lines of neutral technetium.

PECULIAR CARBON STARS (Bidelman).—13 carbon stars have velocities with respect to the sun higher than 100 km/s. The spectra of ten of these have been studied in the blue, and show an exceptional intensity for the CH bands. The lines of hydrogen, of Si II, Ba II and Ti II are also reinforced.

To these "CH stars" correspond the "Ba II stars," characterized by the unusual strength of Ba II 4554. The increase in CH is less than in the preceding stars, and the velocities are moderate.

Another extreme case is represented by the carbon stars weak in hydrogen, whose velocities are also low. The Balmer lines are weak or absent, while those of CI, OI and NI are strong. In these stars the ratio C^{13}/C^{12} is a great deal smaller than in the other C stars (in the order of 1/30 to 1/90).

CHAPTER VI

CONTINUOUS SPECTRA OF THE STARS, GRADIENTS AND COLOR TEMPERATURES

43. Tracing the energy curve by photographic spectrophotometry

Let de be the energy brightness above the atmosphere that a star produces in the spectral interval $d\lambda$. We propose to trace, in relative values, the curve $f(\lambda) = de/d\lambda$. Since the observations are in reality made at ground level, the measured energy must be corrected for atmospheric absorption. It is thus necessary to determine by Bouguer's method (§ 5) the density of the atmosphere at the zenith for a large number of wavelengths.

The energies being measured are generally much too small to permit the use of a thermal receptor. However, Abbot has been able to trace directly the energy curves of a small number of bright stars by means of very delicate radiometers. In one of his last models, the vanes of the radiometer were fragments of fly's wings painted black, having a surface of 0.4 mm². Complete with the mirror that served to record the deviations, the moving equipment weighed a little less than a milligram. It was suspended by a quartz hair 20 cm long inside a silicon tube containing hydrogen under a pressure of 0.2 mm of mercury. The flux received by the 100-inch telescope at Mt. Wilson was dispersed by a slitless spectrograph having a single flint prism and the spectrum was cast onto one of the radiometer vanes. Measurements have been made from 0.437 to 2.224 μ on 18 stars as well as on the planets Mars and Jupiter. The resulting precision was of the order of 10% for the faintest star (β Peg, spectrum M2 II–III). Naturally the measurements were corrected for the loss of light, variable with respect to wavelength in the telescope-spectrograph system and for the increasing dispersion toward the violet.

Selective receivers permit the comparison of the energy transported by radiation in different wavelengths only if their spectral sensitivity curve is known. Photoelectric cells have been used only little up to now for such measurements (§ 26) and at present the study of continuous stellar spectra still depends almost exclusively on photographic photometry. Now, the sensitivity curve for a plate of some determined type is not given absolutely: it depends on the illumination, on the development, etc. To eliminate this difficulty one must compare, wavelength by wavelength, the radiation of a star with that from a laboratory standard, for example, a black body with known temperature. Since one works in both cases with the same dispersing equipment, its spectral transparency and dispersion curve are not involved.

It is a matter of evaluating the ratio of monochromatic intensities e and e' relative to the same wavelengths in the spectra of the two sources, photographed on the same plate, starting from the optical densities measured on the spectra. We are here no longer concerned with point images as in § 12, but with spectra widened during the exposure (§ 24), and we can apply the usual methods of photographic photometry.

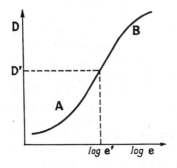

Fig. 25.   Characteristic curve.

The blackening of a plate exposed to a monochromatic radiation depends not only on the intensity but also on the duration of exposure and on the development. The surest method for going from densities to intensities is that which involves the complex laws of blackening of plates as little as possible [23]. We rely on the following principle: two monochromatic intensities of the same wavelength are equal if they produce at two neighboring points of the same plate equal densities for equal exposure times.

The *characteristic curve* of blackening (for variable intensity at a constant exposure time) serves only as an interpolation curve to avoid long trials. We obtain the useful part of this curve by reducing one of the comparison intensities, e, for example, in a series of known ratios. The curve has the behavior represented in Figure 25, where log e is placed on the abscissa and the density D on the ordinate.   It is best for the values to fall on the quasi-linear region AB where the interpolation is surer and the precision greater, since then a variation in log e corresponds to the greatest possible variation in D (maximum contrast).   We thus find for what value of the reduction factor the intensity e would give, with the same exposure time, the same density D' as the intensity e'.   Whenever it is inconvenient to vary one of the two comparison intensities, we can trace the characteristic curve with an auxiliary source.

All measurements of photographic photometry thus involve the measuring of densities on the photograph and the tracing of the characteristic curve from the graduated intensities.

44. Technique of measurement

The measurement of densities on the spectrograms is always made by means of a recording *microphotometer* (or *microdensitometer*) [23], which furnishes a diagram analogous to those of Figures 17 to 19. The abscissas, proportional to those of the spectrogram (parallel to the dispersion) are amplified in a known ratio; the ordinates measure at each point the transmission factor of the plate.

Photometric standardization.—The characteristic curve should be constructed for a rather large number of radiations, because its form varies more or less with wavelength [23].   This standardization is often realized in the laboratory, as far as possible with a *neutral* reduction procedure (weakening all the radiation in the same ratio). One of the simplest procedures, utilized by Chalonge and his collaborators, consists of making a series of successive spectrum exposures of the same duration (of the order of magnitude of the exposures on the stars) on the plate with the comparison spectra.   They place in front of the prism rectangular diaphragms of the same width (in order not to modify the resolution) but of various lengths along the height of the prism, and they illuminate the slit of the spectrograph with a constant intensity source.

The *penumbral photometer*, perfected by Barbier, has the advantage of obtaining the standardization by means of a single exposure.   Let O be the collimator objective of a spectrograph (Fig. 26a), F_1F_2 the uniformly illuminated slit situated in the plane of the figure, and A the straight axis of a diaphragm D which comes just even with the optical axis.   The point F_1 of the slit illuminates all the height of the diaphragm D' placed in front of the objective, whereas the rays issuing from F_2 are completely stopped by the diaphragm D.   Thus the images of the slit on the plate are shaded.   The law of variation of intensity depends on the form of the diaphragm D' placed in front of the objective O. Barbier takes a diaphragm limited by two exponential curves (Fig. 26b). Under these conditions, the logarithm of the brightness is proportional to the abscissa x measured perpendicular to the dispersion.

The penumbral photometer is used most often with a rather wide slit, illuminated by a source emitting a sufficient number of bright lines (tube of mercury, neon, helium or other gas) and the characteristic curves are traced for each of the lines with as many points as are desired.

To standardize photographs obtained with an objective prism by using the stars themselves in a single exposure, a grid has often been

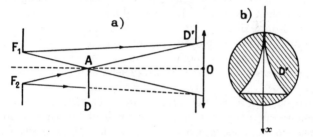

Fig. 26. Schematic arrangement of a penumbral photometer.

placed in front of the prism with the wires perpendicular to the prism apex. The grid functions as a low dispersion grating, and each radiation gives on both sides of the central image diffraction images weakened by a known ratio. If a is the width of the opening between the wires or strips of width b, the intensity of the diffracted image of order p is

$$\sin^2\left(p\pi\,\frac{a}{a+b}\right)\Big/\left(p\pi\,\frac{a}{a+b}\right)^2,$$

where the intensity of the central image is taken as unity. The central spectrum is thus flanked by diffraction spectra (slightly curved on account of the dispersion of the grid grating). With this device one photographs the stars and a comparison source which is very distant or placed at the focus of a collimating lens. In practice, one sees only the first order diffraction spectra; besides, when a is made equal to b the even order spectra disappear. Measurement of the densities in the central spectrum and diffraction spectra of the first order furnish only two points for the characteristic curve for each wavelength. However, certain artifices permit the tracing of the curve.

COMPARISON SOURCES.—All the measurements are ultimately connected with a black body of known temperature. But in general it is preferable to operate in two steps: the star is compared with some much more manageable auxiliary source, which is in turn compared to the black body.

In the visible and near infrared the auxiliary source can be a lamp having a filament or ribbon of tungsten. But its temperature is relatively low ($\simeq 2700°$ K) and the maximum of the energy curve is found at the beginning of the infrared. The maximum of the energy curve for hot stars (O, B, A) is, on the other hand, situated in the ultraviolet and is often unobservable through the earth's atmosphere ($\lambda < 0.3\,\mu$). In its accessible part, the star's curve increases constantly toward the small wavelengths, while that of the lamp with the tungsten ribbon decreases. It is very difficult to measure precisely the spectral intensity ratios in such different radiations.

Hydrogen tubes, employed for this purpose by Chalonge and Lambrey, emit the continuous spectrum of the H_2 molecule, whose intensity increases toward the short wavelengths up to at least 2200 A. They have been used to advantage for the study of ultraviolet stellar spectra (Barbier, Chalonge and Vassy). Chalonge is now using fluorescent sources of weak luminance, made of a mixture of powders (mineral salt crystals) prepared by Servigne. Placed between two layers of quartz, they emit a continuous spectrum extending from 2800 to more than 7000 A when radiated by an ultraviolet mercury lamp (with the resonance line 2537 A and neighboring lines). An appropriate mixture gives an energy curve comparable to those of the stars studied and which depends very little on the composition or on the intensity of the exciting radiation.

45. Photometric study of lines: profiles and equivalent widths

Photographic spectrophotometry is applied also to the study of spectral lines. By means of the characteristic curve we can, in principle, pass from a large scale microphotometer tracing to the energy distribution curve within a rather broad line. We obtain a contour *ABCDE* (Fig. 27), and the area *S* falling between the curve and the continuous spectrum *AE*, which is interpolated across the line and taken as unity, measures the total energy absorbed. It is generally expressed by the width $W = MN$ of the rectangle with the same surface *S* and the same height as the continuous spectrum. This is the *equivalent width* of the line, which is evaluated in angstroms or milliangstroms.

Even with an optically perfect spectrograph the *profile ABCDE* is always more or less altered by instrumental effects, which tend for the most part to diminish the contrast: the finite width of the spectrograph slit and the microphotometer slit, light diffused by the optical pieces (especially the gratings), the diffusion of light in the photographic emulsion. It is therefore necessary to study the instrumental profile that the apparatus imposes on a very sharp line and to compute a correction to the observed profiles.

The equivalent width is much less affected by these parasitic effects than the profile itself and can be measured with a moderate dispersion. To evaluate the equivalent widths of the Balmer lines on spectra of very low dispersion (§ 37), Öhman uses a very large analysis slit (corresponding to a score of angstroms), which receives the entire

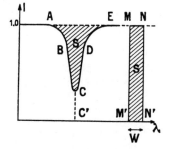

FIG. 27. DEFINITION OF THE EQUIVALENT WIDTH OF A LINE.

image of the line including the wings, and he compares the magnitudes obtained when the slit is centered on the line or placed on either side. For example, he takes as the measure of the Hδ line

$$\Delta m = m_{H\delta} - \tfrac{1}{2}(m_{4140} + m_{4050}),$$

which is a well defined function of the equivalent width. This method, analogous to that of Schilt for the measurement of stellar images (§ 12), must of course be standardized by measuring the equivalent widths of several lines photographed with a large dispersion.

46. Definition of color temperature

Whenever possible, it is convenient to use a single parameter for characterizing the energy distribution curve of a source in a given spectral interval. This parameter is the *color temperature*, which we will define below.

The classical Planck formula expresses the *spectral radiance* of a black body as a function of absolute temperature T and the wavelength λ (§ 3):

$$\rho_\lambda = \frac{d\mathscr{R}}{d\lambda} = 2\pi hc^2\lambda^{-5}(e^{hc/k\lambda T} - 1)^{-1}. \qquad (46.1)$$

In this formula e is the base of the natural logarithms, c the velocity of light in a vacuum, h and k the Planck and Boltzmann constants. With λ in cm, ρ_λ is expressed in erg$\cdot$s$^{-1}\cdot$cm^{-3}.

In view of the numerical applications one can write simply

$$p_\lambda = C_1\sigma^5(e^{C_2\sigma/T} - 1)^{-1}, \qquad (46.1a)$$

where

$\sigma = 1/\lambda$ (wave number in cm)

$C_1 = 2\pi hc^2 = 3.740 \times 10^{-5}$ erg$\cdot$cm$^2\cdot$s^{-1}

$C_2 = hc/k = 1.4385$ cm$\cdot$degree K.

The curves representing the variations of ρ_λ as a function of λ (or of σ) for various temperatures all have the same behavior. They exhibit a maximum for the wavelength λ_m such that

$$\lambda_m T = 0.2897 \text{ cm}\cdot\text{degree (Wien's law)}, \qquad (46.2)$$

so that the maximum is displaced toward the ultraviolet as the temperature increases. On the two sides of the maximum the curves are asymmetric and fall more quickly toward the small wavelengths.

When $C_2\sigma/T$ is rather large, we can neglect the number one subtracted from the exponential and write

$$\rho_\lambda = C_1\sigma^5 e^{-(C_2\sigma/T)}. \qquad (46.3)$$

This is *Wien's approximation*, which gives values approaching nearly 1% when the wavelength considered is less than $1.1\lambda_m$.

Let us now trace by means of (46.1a) the grid of curves representing the spectral energy distribution of a black body at various temperatures. Observations have given us, in relative values, the energy curve of a source studied in a certain spectral region. Now we can try to superimpose it on the black body curves, by multiplying all its ordinates with some arbitrary factor. If the curve coincides rather well with that of the black body having the temperature T_c, this temperature is, by definition, the *color temperature* of the source in the spectral region considered.

When the energy curve of the source does not sufficiently resemble that of the black body, its color temperature cannot be defined.

47. Absolute and relative gradients

We have obtained as photometric measurements for a certain number of wavelengths the magnitude difference $m_2 - m_1$ (above the atmosphere) between a star being studied and a comparison source, which is a black body or a source whose energy curve resembles that of a black body at temperature T_1. We propose to evaluate the color temperature T_2 of the star. It is convenient for this purpose to employ both the *relative gradient* and the function $\Phi(T)$, called the absolute gradient.

The measurements apply to the monochromatic brightnesses. In the case of a black body of spectral luminance b_1, viewed with the apparent diameter α_1, the monochromatic brightness will be written (with a subscript for λ)

$$e_1 = \pi b_1 \alpha_1^2 / 4 = \rho_1 \alpha_1^2 / 4$$

since the black body radiation follows Lambert's law (§ 3). For the star, assumed spherical and viewed with an apparent diameter α_2, we have likewise (§ 3):

$$e_2 = \rho_2 \alpha_2^2 / 4,$$

so that

$$\frac{e_2}{e_1} = \frac{\rho_2}{\rho_1} \left(\frac{\alpha_2}{\alpha_1}\right)^2.$$

If the energy curve of the star is similar, in the spectral region studied, to that of the black body of temperature T_2, we find, in applying Planck's law (46.1a)

$$\frac{e_2}{e_1} = \frac{e^{C_2 \sigma / T_1} - 1}{e^{C_2 \sigma / T_2} - 1} \left(\frac{\alpha_2}{\alpha_1}\right)^2$$

from which the monochromatic magnitude difference is

$$m_2 - m_1 = 2.5[\log (e^{C_2 \sigma / T_2} - 1) - \log (e^{C_2 \sigma / T_1} - 1)] - 5 \log (\alpha_2/\alpha_1).$$

The last term, independent of wavelength and temperature, is moreover in general unknown.

Let us take the derivative of $m_2 - m_1$ with respect to σ and let us note that

$$\frac{d}{d\sigma} [\log (e^{C_2 \sigma / T} - 1)] = \frac{\log_{10} e}{e^{C_2 \sigma / T} - 1} \frac{d}{d\sigma} (e^{C_2 \sigma / T} - 1)$$

$$= \log_{10} e \frac{C_2}{T} (1 - e^{-(C_2 \sigma / T)})^{-1}.$$

In setting

$$\Phi(T) = \frac{C_2}{T} \left(1 - e^{-(C_2\sigma/T)}\right)^{-1},$$

we obtain

$$\frac{d(m_2 - m_1)}{d\sigma} = 2.5 \log_{10} e \times [\Phi(T_2) - \Phi(T_1)]. \qquad (47.1)$$

The quantity

$$G_{2,1} = \frac{d(m_2 - m_1)}{d\sigma} \frac{1}{2.5 \log_{10} e} = 0.921 \frac{d(m_2 - m_1)}{d\sigma}$$

is called the *relative gradient* of source 2 with respect to source 1.

From (47.1) it has the form

$$G_{2,1} = \Phi(T_2) - \Phi(T_1). \qquad (47.2)$$

The relative gradient of source 2 with respect to source 1 is the difference of their absolute gradients.

Now the relative gradient always varies sufficiently slowly with wavelength so that one can consider it as independent of wavelength in a relatively extended spectral interval. It is this property that creates its interest.[1]

When the relative gradient is practically constant in a certain spectral interval, the monochromatic magnitude difference is a linear function of σ. From this a very simple graphical construction results:

We place on the abscissa the wave numbers σ, on the ordinates the magnitude differences $m_2 - m_1$; the points must fall on a straight line of slope $G_{2,1}/0.921$. It is sufficient to add to $\Phi(T_1)$ the relative gradient found in order to obtain $\Phi(T_2)$ and from it, T_2.

If the points do not fall on a straight line, one must conclude that the energy curve of the star differs from a black body curve in the spectral region studied.

[1] The relative gradient of a black body at 10,000° K with respect to one at 4000° K is:

$$G_{2,1} = 1.52 - 4.77 = -3.25 \quad \text{for} \quad \lambda = 5000 \text{ A}$$
$$= 1.48 - 4.77 = -3.29 \qquad\qquad 4250$$
$$= 1.48 - 4.77 = -3.29 \qquad\qquad 3750.$$

When Wien's formula (46.3) furnishes a sufficient approximation, the wave numbers vanish in the expressions for the absolute and relative gradients, which become

$$\Phi(T) = \frac{C_2}{T}, \qquad G_{2,1} = \frac{C_2}{T_2} - \frac{C_2}{T_1}.$$

48. General results: gradients and mean color temperatures for various spectral types

Nowadays we characterize the continuous spectrum of a star more easily by the gradient $\Phi(T_c)$ than by the color temperature T_c itself. In fact, the uncertainty in T_c increases enormously as the gradient diminishes. Thus measurements of equal precision lead to color temperatures of greater uncertainty as they are raised. When, for example, around $\lambda = 0.5\,\mu$, $\Phi(T)$ decreases from 3.10 to 3.00, the color temperature is augmented by 150° (from 4610 to 4760° K), but when Φ diminishes from 0.80 to 0.70, T_c increases 11,800° (from 28,200 to 40,000° K); $\Phi(T)$ tends towards a finite limit as T_i increases indefinitely.

Moreover, the measurement of the relative gradient can itself be difficult for very hot stars, whose spectral radiance is a maximum in an inaccessible ultraviolet region. Furthermore, the energy curve of these generally distant stars is frequently altered by interstellar absorption (§ 50). In the case of cooler stars, another very important cause of error can systematically falsify the measurements: the growing number of absorption lines makes it very difficult to mark the continuous spectrum, which is actually only accessible with moderate dispersion in some narrow "windows." As the number and intensity of the lines increase toward the ultraviolet, the color temperatures determined with insufficient resolution may be too low.

Since the early work of Rosenberg, then of Sampson and of H. H. Plaskett, the determination of gradients has been the object of numerous researches. Greaves, Davidson and Martin at Greenwich, Kienle and his collaborators at Göttingen and then at Heidelberg, used objective prisms and the standardization of the exposures by means of a diffraction grid (§ 44). In France, Barbier, Chalonge and their collaborators at first used small quartz objective prisms whose objective was a simple lens inclined several degrees from the plane normal to the optical axis, in order to enlarge the spectra by astigmatism (A. Couder). The standardization was accomplished with diaphragms on a tube of hydrogen. Their measurements commend themselves by the extreme pains taken with the photometric measurements and the corrections for atmospheric absorption, effected each night by Bouguer's method. The absorption was further reduced to the altitude of the Jungfraujoch (3657 m) where the observations were made. These studies have been carried out for 200 stars, belonging for the most part to classes B and A. The authors measured the gradient Φ_b on the blue side of the Balmer discontinuity (3700 to 4600 A) and the gradient Φ_{uv} on the ultraviolet side (3150 to 3700 A), and at the same time the *size* and *position* of the discontinuity (§ 52).

A new series of observations has been undertaken for about a dozen years now by Chalonge, Mlle. Divan and their team, by means of a slit spectrograph whose plate holder oscillates in order to widen the spectra (§ 24). The standardization is still made with diaphragms, but with a fluorescent source (§ 44).

Table IV summarizes a group of measurements published by Chalonge and his associates (1941 and 1952) for the mean gradients $\Phi_b(\bar\lambda = 0.425\ \mu,\ \bar\sigma = 2.553\ \mu^{-1})$ and color temperatures T_c of different types on the main sequence up to F8 V. The color temperatures are represented on Figure 28 by large black points, following a logarithmic scale. It is not absolutely certain that the temperature maximum observed around type B1 is real. It might result from an insufficient elimination of interstellar absorption.

TABLE IV

"BLUE" GRADIENTS AND CORRESPONDING
COLOR TEMPERATURES

Spectra	Φ_b	T_c (°K)	Spectra	Φ_b	T_c (°K)
O9 V	0.79	24,000	A1 V	1.09	14,600
O9.5–B0	0.74	27,400	A2	1.15	13,600
B0.5–B1	0.73	28,100	A3	1.22	12,600
B2	0.74	27,400	A5	1.34	11,300
B3	0.78	24,600	A7	1.44	10,300
B5	0.90	19,500	F0	1.62	9,100
B8	0.92	18,600	F2	1.77	8,200
B9	0.96	17,500	F5	2.00	7,300
A0 V	1.03	15,800	F6	2.21	6,550
			F8 V	2.30	6,000

The ultraviolet gradient Φ_{uv} ($\bar\lambda = 0.350\ \mu,\ \bar\sigma = 2.85\ \mu^{-1}$) is higher than the blue gradient up to type F0 (except for the O9 stars); then $T_{uv} < T_b$. This is the reverse of the situation after type F5 ($T_{uv} > T_b$).

The measurements of Chalonge and his team are the most complete available for the hot stars. They agree well as a group with those of Göttingen and of Greenwich, which cover somewhat different spectral regions.

The color temperatures determined by spectrophotometry are more uncertain beginning with type G0, because of the importance of absorption lines. According to all observers, the giants have a noticeably lower temperature than the dwarfs, conforming with the qualitative observations of Adams and Kohlschütter (§ 36); the difference can reach a thousand degrees in the classes G and K.

DEVIATIONS FROM A BLACK BODY.—For the stars A7 to F0 and probably for later types such as the sun, the similarity of the energy curve to that of a black body seems valid as a first approximation in a rather large spectral region. The apparent deviations noticed for G stars where the absorption lines are very numerous usually arise from an insufficient resolution.

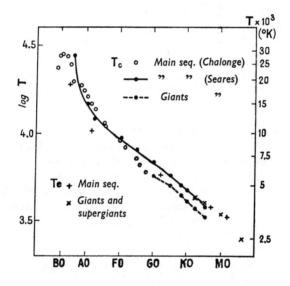

FIG. 28. MEAN COLOR TEMPERATURES T_c AND EFFECTIVE TEMPERATURES T_e FOR THE DIFFERENT SPECTRAL TYPES.

In the case of hot stars, very important deviations in the reverse sense have been found by Jensen and by Kienle, and precisely determined by Berger, Chalonge and Mlles. Divan and Fringant. The measurements give a higher color temperature in the visible than in the blue and violet. Thus, when a very hot star, such as S Mon (type O7), is compared with a star analogous to the sun, such as 47 UMa (G0), we find that on the graph of $1/\lambda$ the points agree well only for $\sigma = 1/\lambda > 2.15\,\mu^{-1}$ and, around 4800 A, sort of a discontinuity appears (Fig. 29).

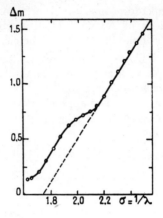

FIG. 29.   MAGNITUDE DIFFERENCE Δ_m BETWEEN THE STARS 47 UMa (G0) AND
S Mon (O6) AS A FUNCTION OF $1/\lambda$ (after CHALONGE).

49. Color indices and temperatures

In the absence of spectrophotometric measurements, knowledge of
the color index of a star can lead to an evaluation of the color
temperature.   Let us first suppose that we measure for two radiations
of wave numbers σ and σ' the monochromatic magnitude difference
between stars 2 and 1.   The corresponding color index is $C = m_2 - m_1$.
If each of the energy curves is similar to that of a black body, we know
that (§ 47)

$$\frac{\mathrm{d}(m_2 - m_1)}{\mathrm{d}\sigma} = C^{\text{te}} = \frac{C}{\sigma - \sigma'} = \frac{1}{0.921}\, G_{2,1}.$$

Measuring the color index C for the two radiations thus is tanta-
mount to determining the relative gradient $G_{2,1}$ between the two stars,
but with only two points, which obviously prevents checking the
constancy of $\mathrm{d}(m_2 - m_1)\,\mathrm{d}\sigma$.[1]
When the measurements apply to rather wide spectral bands, we
can still argue in a first approximation as if they were monochromatic
measurements made at the corresponding *effective wavelengths* (§ 14).
Taking into account the variations as a function of wavelength for
the effective wavelengths of the international photographic and photo-

[1] It is, in fact, by this procedure that Greaves evaluated the gradients. · At
Uppsala they measure in the same way the monochromatic color indices between
wavelengths 0.395 and 0.440 μ on low dispersion spectrograms.

visual system, Seares and Miss Joyner have calculated the theoretical color indices for black bodies of various temperatures and have compared them to the international indices. These are zero in the mean for the A5 stars (and not A0), whose color temperature the authors fixed at 11,000° K according to the spectrophotometric measurements.

The curves of Figure 28, a continuous line for the main sequence and a broken line for the giants, represent the color temperatures thus obtained. As a whole they agree rather well with the temperatures found from spectrophotometric measurements. The semi-empirical formula

$$T_c = \frac{7984}{C + 0.735} \ (^\circ\text{K}),$$

where C is the international color index, allows us, moreover, to find the temperatures given by Seares and Joyner with an error of less than 100° between types A0 and K2.

CHAPTER VII

SPECTROPHOTOMETRIC CLASSIFICATIONS OF STARS

I. INTERSTELLAR ABSORPTION, GRADIENTS AND COLOR INDICES

50. The absorption curve of interstellar clouds

The gradients and color·indices used in the preceding sections concern in principle those stars whose radiation is unaffected by interstellar absorption. Increasing in effect from the infrared to the ultraviolet, this latter phenomenon deforms the energy curves, making the stars appear redder.

In order to study the absorption variations as a function of wave number we must compare, wavelength by wavelength, a *reddened* star with an *unreddened* star of the same spectral type and luminosity class.[1] The differences in the monochromatic magnitudes $m_2(\sigma) - m_1(\sigma)$ between the two stars equal the value $A_2(\sigma)$ of the interstellar absorption in front of the reddened star plus an unknown constant K_2 (which depends on the distance of the stars):

$$m_2(\sigma) - m_1(\sigma) = A_2(\sigma) + K_2.$$

But an important question immediately arises: Is the absorption curve the same for all the clouds of the Galaxy, or not?

In the affirmative, the absorption $A(\sigma)$ can be considered as the product of two factors: the mass M of the absorbing material in a column of unit cross section in the line of sight and the absorption coefficient $a(\sigma)$ per unit mass. In comparing two stars 2 and 3 of different reddening, to the same unreddened star 1, we then have:

$$m_2(\sigma) - m_1(\sigma) = M_2 a(\sigma) + K_2,$$
$$m_3(\sigma) - m_1(\sigma) = M_3 a(\sigma) + K_3.$$

[1] In the case of early B stars, which are considered the most frequently, the energy distribution appears nearly independent of absolute magnitude.

The elimination of $a(\sigma)$ between these two equations gives

$$m_3(\sigma) - m_1(\sigma) = \frac{M_3}{M_2}[m_2(\sigma) - m_1(\sigma)] + K_3 - \frac{M_3}{M_2}K_2.$$

The variation of $m_3(\sigma) - m_1(\sigma)$ as a function of $m_2(\sigma) - m_1(\sigma)$ is represented by a line whose slope measures the ratio M_3/M_2 of the masses of interstellar material. This linear relation does not exist if the function $a(\sigma)$ is not the same for the two stars. The problem can thus be resolved by comparing a rather large number of reddened and unreddened stars situated in diverse regions of the Galaxy.

According to the 6-color photoelectric measurements of Stebbins and Whitford (§ 18), the same absorption curve seems to apply satisfactorily to all the galactic regions except for the Trapezium in the Orion Nebula (1943). But Mlle. Divan has shown that this anomaly is perhaps only apparent. It can be explained at least to a great

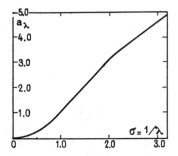

Fig. 30. Interstellar absorption curve, after the measurements of Mlle. Divan and those of Whitford.

extent by the errors that the radiation of the nebulosity introduces into the photometric measurements. The deviations are in fact larger for the fainter stars.

Figure 30 shows the absorption curve traced by Mlle. Divan (1954) for the wavelengths shorter than $0.59\,\mu$ ($\sigma > 1.7\,\mu^{-1}$), extended toward the infrared by means of the most recent measurements of Whitford (1958). Here we shall not study the interstellar material for its own sake, but only on account of the complications that its presence introduces into the measurement of gradients and color indices. Let us limit ourselves to pointing out that the form of the curve can be accounted for by attributing the apparent absorption to the diffusion of starlight by solid grains of dimensions comparable to the visible wavelengths and whose refractive index can be in the vicinity of that of ice (1.33). It is generally believed to be caused in fact by crystals of impure ice (H_2O) containing such molecules as H_2, NH_3, CH_4, MgH and undoubtedly a very small number of heavy atoms (van de Hulst) [12].

51. Applications to spectral classification

The absorption curve presents a rather straight segment for around $\sigma > 2.1\ \mu^{-1}$ ($\lambda < 0.48\ \mu$) and a second almost straight segment of greater slope in the visible region; it then curves inward and flattens in the near infrared where its shape, based on measurements made with a Pb-S cell, is less sure.

In a straight or quasi straight domain the magnitude difference between a reddened and an unreddened star is a linear function of σ, since it acts as if the two stars involved were of different color temperatures (§ 47). If the radiation of each star could be characterized throughout the observable spectrum by a unique gradient, it would be very difficult to distinguish the temperature effects from those of absorption. In fact, the separation is possible because the energy curves differ sufficiently from those of black bodies.

THE DIFFERENCE BETWEEN VISIBLE AND ULTRAVIOLET GRADIENTS.— The absolute gradients Φ_b and Φ_{uv} of an unreddened star, determined on each side of the Balmer discontinuity, are, in general, different (§ 48). But since both are measured in the straight region of the curve $a(\sigma)$ ($\sigma > 2.1$), the interstellar absorption has the effect of increasing the two gradients by the same amount. *The difference $\Phi_b - \Phi_{uv}$ is thus completely independent of absorption*; this is an intrinsic characteristic of the stars.

Mlle. Divan has established, in determining a "visible" gradient Φ_{vis} between 0.39 and 0.61 μ, that the difference $\Phi_{vis} - \Phi_{uv}$ for practical purposes depends only on the spectral type between O6 and at least B3, and can serve to determine the type exactly. It varies from -0.19 in type O6 to $+0.05$ in type B3.

THREE-COLOR PHOTOMETRY.—Three- or six-color photometry is devised to take advantage of the change in gradient observed around 0.49 μ. The photographic measurements of W. Becker are made in three spectral regions centered on 0.380, 0.475 and 0.620 μ. Becker (1941) has shown that, for all spectral types, the difference

$$C = (m_{0.380} - m_{0.475}) - (m_{0.475} - m_{0.620})$$

is practically independent of interstellar absorption; it has been useful for determining the spectral types in numerous galactic clusters.

The photoelectric measurements made in the U–B–V system (§ 18) lend themselves to an analogous application. An unreddened star is characterized by the *intrinsic* indices $(B-V)_0$ and $(U-B)_0$, of which at least the first is closely connected with the spectral type (Fig. 31). On a reddened star we measure the indices

$$B - V = (B - V)_0 + E_{B-V},$$

$$U - B = (U - B)_0 + E_{U-B},$$

where E_{B-V} and E_{U-B} represent the *color excess* due to absorption. The law of interstellar absorption imposes a constant value on the ratio E_{U-B}/E_{B-V}, which, according to the measurements of Johnson and Morgan on 290 O and B stars, is 0.72 ± 0.03.

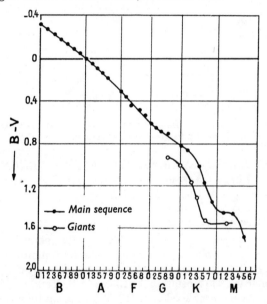

Fig. 31. B–V color indices as a function of spectral type for non-red stars (Johnson and Morgan).

It therefore happens that the quantity Q, defined by

$$Q = (U - B) - \frac{E_{U-B}}{E_{B-V}} (B - V)$$

$$= (U - B)_0 - 0.72(B - V)_0,$$

is independent of interstellar absorption. The quantity Q diminishes rapidly from type B0 to type A0 (from -0.85 to -0.44) and permits the precise classification of B stars (Fig. 32).

Q and $(B - V)_0$ being connected to the spectral type, there exists a close relation between these two quantities. The observational data lead to a linear relation, which permits the color excess E_{B-V} to be expressed as a function of Q and of the measured B–V index:

$$E_{B-V} = (B - V) - (B - V)_0 = (B - V) - 0.337Q + 0.009.$$

Thus 3-color photometry in the U–B–V system leads simultaneously to the precise determination of spectral type and of reddening for the B stars.

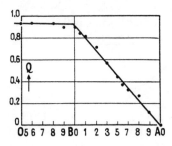

FIG. 32.   VARIATION IN THE QUANTITY Q AS A FUNCTION OF SPECTRAL TYPE (after JOHNSON and MORGAN).

II. SPECTRAL CLASSIFICATIONS OF TWO DIMENSIONS (BARBIER AND CHALONGE) AND OF THREE DIMENSIONS (CHALONGE AND DIVAN)

52. Definition of parameters [24, 27, 28]

A method of spectral classification having two parameters, based solely on the spectrophotometric study of the continuous spectrum in the vicinity of the Balmer discontinuity, was developed by Barbier and Chalonge in 1939 for stars of the classes O, B, A and F. Chalonge and Mlle. Divan completed it in 1953 by the addition of a third parameter.

The continuous spectrum that extends the Balmer series toward the ultraviolet (§ 29) appears weakly in absorption in the later O types. Its intensity increases in class B and reaches a maximum around types A0–A2 in the main sequence and around type F0 for supergiants; it then diminishes and vanishes in class G. On the other hand, the Balmer continuum is visible in emission in those B stars that also show the first Balmer lines in emission.

The first two parameters are the *size* and *position* of the discontinuity that marks the beginning of the absorption (or emission) continuous spectrum. On a microphotometer tracing such as that shown in Figure 33a one joins by a continuous curve *ABDE* the points corresponding to the greatest photographic densities between the lines. The portions *AB* and *DE* correspond to the intensity of the continuum itself, but it is impossible to attach a precise significance to the intermediate part of the tracing, *BD* (especially when working with low dispersion), on account of the overlapping of the last Balmer lines.

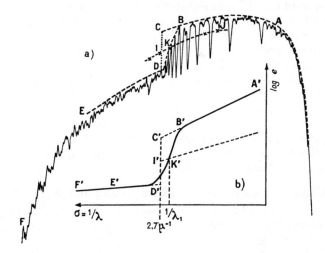

FIG. 33. MAGNITUDE AND POSITION OF THE BALMER DISCONTINUITY.

Beginning with the measurements made on the tracing, we obtain, with the aid of black body curves, the logarithms of the relative intensities for different points along the tracing and we construct the graph representing $\log e$ as a function of $\sigma = 1/\lambda$ (Fig. 33b). The same letters designate the corresponding points on Figures 33a and 33b. For stars of type earlier than G0, the segments $A'B'$ and $D'F'$ (Fig. 33b) are rather straight. Let us extend these up to points C' and D' respectively where they cut the vertical that has the abscissa $\sigma = 2.70\ \mu^{-1}$ ($\lambda = 0.370\ \mu$) and let us read the corresponding intensities. By definition, the size of the Balmer discontinuity is the quantity

$$D = \log (e_{C'}/e_{D'}) = \log e_{C'} - \log e_{D'}.$$

The absorption becomes continuous beginning at a longer wavelength λ_0, which is not susceptible to precise measurement. In order to mark the *position* of the discontinuity we substitute for λ_0 a much better defined neighboring wavelength. Let I' be the middle of the vertical segment $C'D'$ (Fig. 33*b*). From this point we draw the line $I'K'$ equally distant from the two continua. It cuts the real curve $B'D'$ at K'. The wavelength λ_1 corresponding to the abscissa σ_1 of the point K' is taken as the measure for the position of the discontinuity. It is displaced, depending on the star, from about 3690 to 3780 A.

The third parameter introduced more recently is the blue gradient Φ_b (§ 48), now measured between wavelengths 3800 and 4800 A. It is affected only by interstellar absorption.

With the spectrograph used by Chalonge and his collaborators, the mean errors for a dozen independent determinations are ± 0.003 for D, ± 1 A for λ_1 and ± 0.03 for Φ_b. When the discontinuity is small, the mean errors reach ± 0.01 for D and ± 3 A for λ_1.

This method achieves, with respect to those which use the relative intensities of lines, the great advantage of only depending on the measurement of three physically well defined parameters, capable of a precise determination even with a low dispersion, and which stay the same for all stars of types O6 to F8.

53. Classification of stars of populations I and II [24, 27, 28]

POPULATION I.—Each star is represented in a three-dimensional plot by a point M having coordinates Φ_b, D and λ_1. The stars of population I that can be classified in the Yerkes system fall in the vicinity of a surface Σ whose shape is represented in Figure 34. On the model of the surface are traced two families of curves: the curves $\Phi_b = C^{te}$ separating the spectral types; the curves of the other family, approximately orthogonal to the first, separating the Yerkes luminosity classes. Thus each curvilinear quadrilateral corresponds to a complete symbol in the MKK system. But the new classification is obviously sharper, since on it one can distinguish, inside each quadrilateral, stars having slightly different characteristics, varying in a continuous manner.

In the early classification of Barbier and Chalonge, the plotted point of a star was the projection of the point M on the D, λ_1 plane. It was then necessary to consider separately the stars now belonging to the left and right parts of the surface Σ, which can have the same D and λ_1 coordinates but a different Φ_b coordinate. In practice, however, these projections are still often used.

If all the stars lay exactly on the surface Σ, the introduction of the third parameter would be useless, at least for population I stars. But in fact this is not so: on each side of the surface these stars occupy a certain volume, whose thickness parallel to the Φ_b axis is about 0.25 to 0.30, safely larger than the errors of measurement. The properties of the stars therefore actually depend on the three parameters.

Metallic line stars (§ 41), practically unclassifiable on the MKK system, fall *behind* the right part of Σ, the distance from the surface depending on how much their "metallic" character is accentuated (Berger, Mlles. Fringant and Menneret).

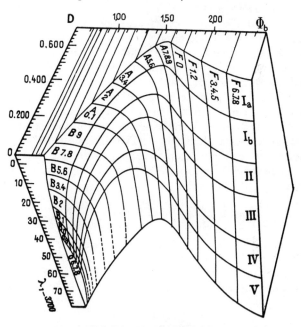

FIG. 34. THE SURFACE Σ.

POPULATION II.—In contrast, the subdwarfs, which belong to population II, are clearly situated *in front* of the right part of the surface Σ.

Miss Roman has divided the stars of types later than F5 into "strong line stars" and "weak line stars." These later stars, having high velocities, can be associated with population II. The strong line stars fall around the limit of the volume occupied by the other population I stars, inside the right part of the surface Σ, that is to say, beside the metallic line stars. The weak line stars are found on the other hand in the vicinity of the other limit of the volume, in front of the right part of Σ, beside the subdwarfs (Mlle. Divan), and indicate the existence of a continuous range between the subdwarfs and the main sequence, that is to say, between populations II and I.

Finally, the variable RR Lyrae, completely characteristic of population II, describes in the course of its cycle of variation a closed counterclockwise curve situated a little in front of the right part of the surface (Mlle. Fringant).

Thus the three-dimensional classification brings a new precision to the classification of population I stars and begins to give indications on those of population II.

Chalonge and his collaborators are especially interested in the "calibration of absolute magnitude," that is, the determination of the function $M = f(\lambda_1, D, \Phi_b)$. The calibration has been able to get started from the knowledge of the trigonometric parallaxes of the nearest dwarfs in class F and has been extended up to A0 by the study of stars belonging to galactic clusters of known distance such as the Hyades. But the most effective method for achieving the calibration of the A and F stars depends on the precise classification of components of visual double stars (J. Berger). The difference ΔM in absolute magnitude between the two components of a system is known exactly, since it equals the difference of their apparent magnitudes. Thus one can write

$$\Delta M = \frac{\partial M}{\partial \lambda_1} \Delta \lambda_1 + \frac{\partial M}{\partial D} \Delta D + \frac{\partial M}{\partial \Phi_b} \Delta \Phi_b,$$

representing by $\Delta \lambda_1$, ΔD and $\Delta \Phi_b$ the differences in coordinates of the plotted points. The study of a rather large number of systems permits the evaluation of the partial derivatives $\partial M/\partial \lambda_1$, $\partial M/\partial D$ and $\partial M/\partial \Phi_b$ and therefore the extension of the calibration from one region to another.

54. Other photometric classifications having two parameters
[24]

In other two-dimensional classifications the size of the Balmer discontinuity is retained as the first parameter, but another parameter is substituted for λ_1, since the determination of λ_1 is somewhat un-certain for O–B0 stars and for types later than F0. Sometimes one takes the observable number of Balmer lines, which requires a higher dispersion; more often the intensity of a line chosen from among those of hydrogen is used.

Thus Mme. Hack (1953) measured on low dispersion spectrograms the apparent central intensity of $H\gamma$ and obtained a classification in good agreement with those of Chalonge and Morgan.

Strömgren (1951–1958) has adopted the total intensity of the $H\beta$ line, isolated with a narrow passband interference filter (passband width at half intensity $\Delta\lambda = 35$ A). Further photoelectric measurements are made with other interference filters on four wider spectral bands ($\Delta\lambda \simeq 80$ to 100 A), centered on 5000, 4700, 4500 and 4030 A, and finally on a very large region ($\Delta\lambda \simeq 350$ A) around 3600 A. The line intensity is characterized by the index

$$l = m_{4861} - \tfrac{1}{2}(m_{5000} + m_{4700}),$$

the size of the Balmer discontinuity by the index

$$c = (m_{3600} - m_{4030}) - (m_{4030} - m_{4500}).$$

The wavelengths are chosen in such a manner that interstellar absorption does not interfere. In addition, no Balmer lines are included in the passbands of the filters at 5000, 4700, 4500 and 4030 A.

On graphs constructed with c on the abscissa and l on the ordinate for types O and B on the one hand, A and F on the other, the supergiants and bright giants (classes I and II) are clearly separated from the less luminous stars; they lie well above the curve corresponding to the main sequence. The metallic line stars are situated a little below the curve. The system has been calibrated in absolute magnitude.

CHAPTER VIII

DIAMETERS AND EFFECTIVE TEMPERATURES OF THE STARS

55. Order of magnitude of apparent diameters

If we can measure the apparent diameter α of a star with known distance r, we immediately obtain its linear diameter

$$2R = r\alpha \quad (\alpha \text{ in radians}).$$

But it is easy to see that the apparent stellar diameters are always extremely small. We can assume in fact that a dwarf star of type G2 V has the same radiance as the sun. We then have, from (3.3)

$$E_*/E_\odot = (\alpha_*/\alpha_\odot)^2.$$

The ratio of stellar brightnesses of the star and the sun is equal to the square of their apparent diameters. If we now compare to the sun ($m_{pv} = -26.73$, $\alpha = 1920''$) the star 16 Cyg A ($m_{pv} = 5.96$), we find:

$$\log (\alpha_*/\alpha_\odot) = \tfrac{1}{2} \log (E_*/E_\odot)$$
$$= -0.2(m_* - m_\odot) = -6.54$$

and

$$\alpha_* \simeq 0''.00055.$$

The apparent diameter of an identical star 10 times closer and therefore 100 times brighter ($m_{pv} \simeq 1.0$) would be 10 times greater. Thus *the apparent diameters of main sequence stars may at the most be in the order of thousandths of a second of arc.*

The case of the giant stars is a little more favorable. If we assume, for example, that with the same radiance a G giant has an intensity 100 times greater than a dwarf of the same type, its linear diameter and therefore its apparent diameter at the same distance must be 10 times greater. Actually the radiance of a giant is a little less than that of a dwarf, since its color temperature is a little lower (§ 48). Its apparent diameter would thus be more than 100 times greater. *The apparent diameter of the nearest late-type giants undoubtedly reaches several hundredths of a second of arc.*

Such a diameter is still inappreciable even with the largest telescopes. The angular radius ϵ of the diffraction spot given by an objective of diameter D cm is effectively, for the wavelength $\lambda = 0.55\,\mu$, $\epsilon = 14''/D$ (§ 10). For the Mount Palomar telescope ($D = 500$ cm) $2\epsilon = 0''.056$, and it would be necessary to have a telescope of 28 m aperture for 2ϵ to be less than $0''.01$. Furthermore, the stellar images are always more or less enlarged by atmospheric turbulence which, under the most favorable conditions, can still be in the order of $0''.1$. Therefore no hope exists for obtaining the apparent diameters of stars from direct measurement by observing their images at the focus of a telescope, no matter how large it is.

56. Principle of interferometric measurement of apparent diameters

The interferometric measurement of apparent stellar diameters, proposed long ago by Fizeau, was accomplished in 1920 by Michelson and Pease. This is an application of Young's classic double slit experiment.

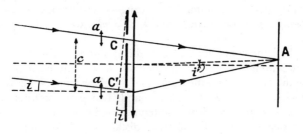

Fig. 35.

A plane wave with an angle of incidence i falls on an opaque screen pierced by two symmetric slits (Fig. 35). A converging objective placed behind the screen permits the observation, in the focal plane, of fringes apparently projected to infinity. One then sees, superimposed on the diffraction figure that would be given by a single slit, a system of straight and equidistant fringes perpendicular to the line CC' joining the two slits. The intensity at some point A lying in the focal plane and corresponding to the angle of emergence i' is thus proportional to

$$F(a, \mu) \cos^2 (\mu c/2) \tag{56.1}$$

where a is the width of each slit along CC', c the separation between two similar points in each slit and

$$\mu = 2 \frac{\pi}{\lambda} (\sin i + \sin i').$$

The first factor of (56.1) determines the appearance of the diffraction bands, which remain when one of the slits is masked, and depends on the shape of the slit.   In all ordinary cases $F(a, \mu)$ tends toward unity as μ tends toward zero.[1]

The second factor $\cos^2 (\mu c/2)$ determines the appearance of the interference fringes (which disappear when one of the slits is masked). They are much more closely spaced than the diffraction bands since in general c is considerably larger than a.

For the very small angles i and i', which are the only ones involved in the present case, we express the angles in radians and write simply

$$\mu = \frac{2\pi}{\lambda} (i + i')$$

and we consider the function $F(a, \mu)$ to be unity.

The interference minima (dark fringes) correspond to $i + i' = (2p + 1)\lambda/2c$ and the maxima to $i + i' = p\lambda/c$ where p is zero or an integer.

The phenomena are in no way modified if any number of luminous points are found at infinity aligned on a straight normal to CC', because the maxima and the minima of the given fringe systems super-impose rigorously.   On the other hand, two point sources aligned parallel to CC' give two fringe systems shifted one from another by a quantity depending on the angular distance δ of the two luminous points.   The contrast of the fringes becomes a minimum when the

---

[1] When we have rectangular slits of width a

$$F(a, \mu) = \sin^2 \left(\frac{\mu a}{2}\right) \Big/ \left(\frac{\mu a}{2}\right)^2.$$

We then observe a bright central image flanked by straight alternating dark and bright bands, obviously fainter and half the width of the central band. When the slits are circles of diameter a, we see very faint rings, practically equidistant, around a bright circular spot of angular diameter $1.22\lambda/a$.   As in the preceding case, the function F tends toward unity as μ approaches zero [5, 6].

maxima of one system coincide with the minima of the other (for $\delta = \lambda/2c$). (On this principle is based the Michelson method for measuring the angular distance and position angle of the components of a double star.) When the apparent diameter of a source is not negligible, the contrast varies with the angular extent of the source in the direction CC'.

Let E_M and E_m be the intensity of the maxima and minima of the interference fringes. The contrast of these is characterized by the quantity

$$V = (E_M - E_m)/(E_M + E_m),$$

called the *visibility* of the fringes. In the case of a point source, the intensity E_m of the minima is zero and $V = 1$. $V = 0$ when the fringes disappear completely.

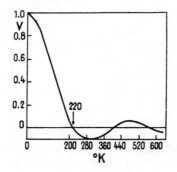

Fig. 36. Visibility curve for the fringes.

In the case of a circular source of angular radius i_0 and of uniform luminance, the calculus leads to the expression

$$V = \frac{4}{\pi} \int_0^1 \sqrt{1 - x^2} \cdot \cos kx \cdot \mathrm{d}x$$

where

$$x = i/i_0 \quad \text{and} \quad k = 2\pi c i_0/\lambda.$$

The integral is calculated by means of Bessel functions of the first order. Figure 36 shows the shape of the visibility curve, drawn with k on the abscissa. When we progressively increase the separation c of the two slits, k increases, the visibility decreases and vanishes when $k = 1.22\pi \simeq 220°$, that is to say, for

$$c = 1.22 \, \lambda/\alpha, \tag{56.2}$$

where by α we designate the apparent diameter $2i_0$ of the source. If we continue increasing c, the fringes reappear, but with much less contrast, the maxima now taking the place of the minima $(V < 0)$; the visibility vanishes again for a larger value of c, etc.

It is probable that in reality the luminance of the stellar disks diminishes from center to limb as the sun's does. The calculation can then be carried out by adopting a limb-darkening law analogous to that for the sun. The visibility of the fringes then vanishes for the first time when k takes a value greater than $1.22\,\pi$. The apparent diameters α calculated by (56.2), with the hypothesis of uniform luminance, are then too small, but the correction is less than 10%.

57. Experiments of Michelson and Pease

The experiment consists of progressively increasing the distance of the openings C and C' until the fringes disappear. When this result is obtained, the apparent diameter of the stellar disk (the luminance assumed uniform) is calculable by the relation (56.2).

In order to find what dimensions to give to the instrument, let us seek the distance c between the openings necessary to make the fringes disappear on a disk of diameter $0''.04$, which is nearly $2 \cdot 10^{-7}$ radian. By taking $\lambda = 0.55\,\mu = 5.5 \cdot 10^{-5}$ cm as the mean wavelength, we have

$$c = 1.22\ \lambda/\alpha = 1.22 \cdot 5.5 \cdot 10^{-5}/2 \cdot 10^{-7} = 335.5 \text{ cm.}$$

The apparatus of Michelson is represented schematically in Figure 37A. An optical bench six meters long was placed at the upper end of the 100-inch telescope at Mt. Wilson, chosen not because of its optical qualities, which make no difference here, but for the strength of its mounting (since vibrations of $1\,\mu$ amplitude would destroy the view of the fringes). The bench carried four plane mirrors of about 15 cm diameter, M_1, M_2, M_3, M_4. The two extremes were movable, the two intermediate ones in principle fixed. After reflecting the light into the declination axis by means of a 45° mirror, Michelson and Pease observed the diffraction spot striated by interference fringes, and they systematically separated the mirrors M_1 and M_4 until the fringes disappeared.

When the mirrors were moved it was impossible to maintain the equality of the optical trains between the two rays that interfered. To remedy this, in one of the paths was placed a compensator formed from two identical glass wedges, which could slide over each other (Fig. 37B). The inequality of the optical paths was thus compensated by varying the thickness of the glass traversed. In the other light path, they placed a plane-parallel glass plate of the same refractive index, whose thickness was equal to the mean thickness of the double wedge (Fig. 37C). The two diffraction figures no longer necessarily superimposed after the mirrors were displaced, owing to the imperfection of the tracks. They then restored the coincidence by slowly tipping the plate in a fashion that laterally displaced the ray that traversed it.

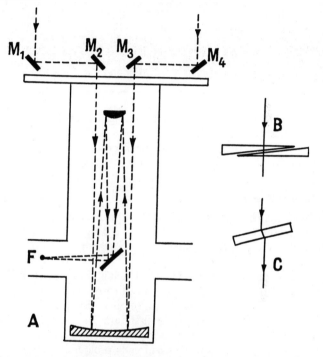

Fig. 37. Schematic plan of the Michelson interferometer.

Experience has shown that the method is not very sensitive to atmospheric seeing conditions: the interference fringes are displaced much less than the stellar images taken as a whole.

The third column of Table V gives the apparent diameters of six giants or supergiants of classes M and K measured by Pease, supposing the disks to have uniform luminance. The fourth column tabulates the apparent diameters calculated according to these measurements by Kuiper, who sought to take into account the probable limb darkening. The correction varies from 2.5 to 9 percent. For an additional

TABLE V

APPARENT DIAMETERS MEASURED WITH
THE INTERFEROMETER

Stars	Spectra	α (")	α_1 (")	r (pc)	2 R (10^8 km)	$R/R_\odot$	m_b	T_e
o Cet	(gM6)	0".048	0".048	250?	(17.9)	(1290)	−0.14	3500
α Ori	M2 I ab	.041	.044	91	6.0	430	−1.59	3660
α Sco	(cM0)	.040	.043	71	4.6	330	−1.24	3410
β Peg	M2 II-III	.021	.022	50	1.8	131	+0.37	3300
α Tau	K5 III	.020	.022	20	0.64	46	−0.44	3970
α Boo	K2 IIIp	0".020	0".022	11.5	0.38	27	−0.80	4310

star, α Her (M5 III), Pease obtained a provisional value $\alpha = +0".021$; finally, in the case of γ And (K0) and of α Ari (K2 III), it was not possible to make the fringes disappear entirely. Their apparent diameters could be around 0".014 and 0".011 respectively.

58. Occultation method

Another method for measuring the apparent diameters of stars depends on the observation of interference fringes which border the geometric shadow at the moment when a star is becoming occulted by the moon.

The shadow of the side of the moon which is about to occult the star moves across the earth with a speed in the order of 1 km/sec. If the star resembles a luminous point, an angular displacement of 0".003 corresponds to the passage from the first dark fringe to the first bright fringe. If the star shows an apparent diameter α_* of that order, the distribution of light in the fringes is already profoundly altered. One can arrive at a value of α_* by recording the variations of brightness that precede the disappearance of a star and by comparing with the theoretical value the brightness observed at the point where the geometric shadow should appear.

In the course of an occultation of Regulus (α Leo, spectrum B7 V), Arnulf succeeded in recording the first two bright fringes on a rapidly moving photographic plate. He obtained a preliminary value for the apparent diameter $\alpha_* = 0".0018$. Scarcely sensitive to seeing conditions, this method allows the finding of apparent diameters inaccessible to interferometry. It has recently been taken up with photoelectric photometry (Evans).

59. Indirect spectrophotometric method

We would immediately obtain the apparent diameter of a star with known brightness if we could evaluate its radiance (3.3).

In a spectral region where the color temperature is well defined, the spectral radiance of a star $\rho_\lambda(*)$ is proportional (but not equal) to that of a black body $\rho_\lambda(T_c)$ at the known temperature T_c. In other words, the star radiates as a "gray body" (§ 76) and we can write

$$\rho_\lambda(*) = p \cdot \rho_\lambda(T_c), \qquad (59.1)$$

where p is a factor independent of wavelength ($p < 1$), which we must determine.

For this purpose we measure the residual intensity $I_{0,\lambda}$ at the center of the first Balmer lines, that is to say, the ratio between the intensities at the bottom of the line and of the continuous spectrum at the same wavelength (Fig. 27, § 45). In the case of radiative equilibrium (§ 76), the radiation arising from the base of a strong line is emitted by a high outer layer whose spectral radiance seems very close to that of the black body $\rho_\lambda(T_0)$ having the surface temperature T_0. The magnitude difference $m_0 - m$ between the bottom of the line and the continuous spectrum is thus a linear function of wave number

$$m_0 - m = -2.5 \log I_{0,\lambda} = f(\sigma).$$

Each of the lines studied gives a point on the line whose slope yields the relative gradient

$$G(T_0, T_c) = \Phi(T_0) - \Phi(T_c)$$

and the surface temperature T_0, since T_c is known.

Thus we can calculate, by the Planck formula, the spectral radiance $\rho_\lambda(T_0)$ for each line, and that of the star is deduced immediately from

$$\rho_\lambda(*) = \rho_\lambda(T_0)/I_0.$$

Substituting in (59.1) the values of $\rho_\lambda(*)$ thus obtained, we get the factor p, which must be the same for all the lines except Hα and Hβ; it is prudent to exclude them on account of possible complications.

Knowledge of the spectral radiance of a star resolves the problem. Let m_* and $m_\odot$ be the magnitudes (photovisual, for example) of the star and of the sun. For the effective wavelength corresponding to these magnitudes, we calculate the spectral radiance of a star by (59.1), where p is now known, and from the relation

$$m_* - m_\odot = -2.5 \log \left[\frac{\rho_*}{\rho_\odot} \left(\frac{\alpha_*}{\alpha_\odot} \right)^2 \right]$$

we find the apparent diameter α_*, the only unknown.

Proposed by Mme. Cayrel, Chalonge and Mlle. Divan (1955), this method, although apparently complex, requires in practice only relatively simple measurements, and it can be applied to a great number of stars of classes O, B, A and F. In the case of the bright component of the Algol eclipsing binary system (β Per, spectrum B8 V, $m_{pv} = 2.3$, $T_c \simeq 26{,}500°$ K), the residual intensities of the Hγ, Hδ and Hϵ lines have given the surface temperature $T_0 = 8700°$ and, finally, an apparent diameter $\alpha_* = 0''.0009$. We find $0''.0008$ by a totally different method, by evaluating, through the study of eclipses (§ 60 and 66), the linear radius of the star ($R_* = 2.7\odot$) whose distance is known ($r = 30$ pc).

60. Linear diameters of the stars

Those stars whose apparent diameter has been measured by interferometry are almost all near enough for trigonometric determinations of their parallaxes to be rather precise. The corresponding distances are given in parsecs in the 5th column of Table V. The most doubtful is that of the variable o Ceti (*Mira Ceti*), whose parallax is quite small. The linear diameters based on these distances and apparent diameters α_1 (corrected as nearly as possible for limb darkening) are expressed in the 6th column in kilometers and, in the 7th, in solar diameters ($2R_\odot = 1.395 \cdot 10^6$ km).

We see that the red supergiants reach enormous dimensions. Among the four stars of class M, the first two have diameters clearly larger and the third a diameter comparable to that of the orbit of the planet Mars ($4.55 \cdot 10^8$ km). The radius of the K giants is still several tens of solar radii.

Let us likewise compare the diameter of the main sequence star α Leo (B7 V) to that of the sun, using the provisional value of the apparent diameter measured by Arnulf ($0''.0018$). Between the radii R, the distances r and the apparent diameters α of the star and the sun, we can write the relation

$$\frac{R_*}{R_\odot} = \frac{r_* \alpha_*}{r_\odot \alpha_\odot}.$$

The distance of Regulus, deduced from its trigonometric parallax, is $r = 24$ pc $= 24 \times 2.06 \cdot 10^5 = 4.9 \cdot 10^6$ astronomical units. Furthermore the apparent diameter of the sun is $\alpha_\odot = 1920''$ and its distance is 1 A.U. Accordingly,

$$\frac{R_*}{R_\odot} = 4.9 \cdot 10^6 \frac{0.0018}{1920} = 4.6.$$

This order of magnitude for a main sequence B star can be confirmed by another method.

The photometric and spectroscopic study of an eclipsing binary system showing two spectra gives in fact a means for evaluating the *linear* diameter of each of the two components (§ 65). We establish that the radii are of the order of the solar radius along the main sequence, but constantly diminish from class O (where they surpass 10 solar radii) to class K (where they are less than 1 solar radius) (Table VI and Fig. 43, § 66). For B3 stars we find a mean of 4.5 ⊙ and for B4–B9 stars, 2.8 ⊙.

A small number of normal giants and bright giants belonging to eclipsing systems lead to radii of a few tens or even hundreds of solar radii.

Thus the terms "giants" and "dwarfs," which up to now have designated stars of large and small luminosity, correspond to the actual geometry.

61. Effective temperatures of stars

The effective temperature (or the radiation temperature) *of some source is, by definition, the temperature of a black body having the same total energy radiance as the source considered.* It is perfectly defined in all cases, even when the radiation of the source differs profoundly from that of a black body, and in particular it does not assume that the energy distribution curve as a function of wavelength resembles that of a black body.

The total energy radiance of a black body, having a temperature $T°$ K for all wavelengths, is given by Stefan's law [14]

$$\mathscr{R} = \sigma T^4, \qquad (61.1)$$

where

$$\sigma = \frac{2\pi^5 k^4}{15c^2 h^3} = 5.6724 \cdot 10^{-5} \text{ ergs} \cdot \text{s}^{-1} \cdot \text{cm}^{-2} \cdot \text{degree}^{-4}.$$

Thus being able to measure the total energy radiance of a source is equivalent to finding its effective temperature.

One evaluates the radiance $\mathscr{R}$:

(*a*) by using the apparent diameter α and the total energy brightness E (or the apparent bolometric magnitude m_b), or

(*b*) by using a linear diameter $2R$ and the total energy intensity I (or the absolute bolometric magnitude M_b).

(a) In the case of a spherical source, whose luminance is at each point the same along the normal, $\mathcal{R}$ is expressed as a function of E and of α by (3.3), whence

$$\mathcal{R} = 4E/\alpha^2.$$

Let us write that this radiance is equal to that of a black body at the temperature T_e. Stefan's law (61.1) gives the effective temperature

$$T_e = \sqrt[4]{\frac{4E}{\sigma\alpha^2}}. \tag{61.2}$$

In this way we calculate the effective temperature of the sun from the total energy brightness which it produces above the terrestrial atmosphere. This quantity, known as the *solar constant*, according to the most recent measurements made at the earth's surface and at high altitudes by means of balloons and rockets, equals

$$E_\odot = 1.595 \cdot 10^6 \text{ erg} \cdot \text{s}^{-1} \cdot \text{cm}^{-2}(2.0 \text{ cal} \cdot \text{gr} \cdot \text{cm}^{-2} \cdot \text{min}^{-1}).$$

With $\alpha_\odot = 1920'' = 0.9308 \cdot 10^{-2}$ radian, we find

$$T_{e\odot} = 5800° \text{ K}.$$

It is convenient to compare other stars to the sun. By successively applying relation (61.2) to two stars and by forming the ratio $T_{e*}/T_{e\odot}$ we get

$$\frac{T_{e*}}{T_{e\odot}} = \sqrt[4]{\frac{E_*}{E_\odot}} \sqrt[2]{\frac{\alpha_\odot}{\alpha_*}},$$

or, by taking the logarithms,

$$\log (T_{e*}/T_{e\odot}) = \frac{1}{4} \log \frac{E_*}{E_\odot} + \frac{1}{2} \log \frac{\alpha_\odot}{\alpha_*}.$$

Finally, by introducing the bolometric magnitudes m_b of the sun and the star

$$\log T_{e*} = \log T_{e\odot} - 0.1(m_{b*} - m_{b\odot}) + 0.5(\log \alpha_\odot - \log \alpha_*).$$

If we express the apparent diameters in seconds of a degree and take

$$\alpha_\odot = 1920'', \qquad m_{b\odot} = -26.79, \qquad T_{e\odot} = 5800° \text{ K},$$

we obtain

$$\log T_{e*} = 2.726 - 0.5 \log \alpha_* - 0.1 \, m_{b*}. \tag{61.3}$$

This relation can be applied immediately to any star whose apparent diameter α_1 has been measured by interferometry. In the next to the last column of Table V are listed the bolometric magnitudes based on the thermal measurements of Pettit and Nicholson (§ 21 and 22). The effective temperatures obtained are displayed in the last column.

(*b*) The total energy intensity I is linked to the brightness E by the fundamental relation (2.1), which, by introducing the radius R and the apparent diameter α in radians, can be written

$$I = 4ER^2/\alpha^2,$$

or, by using (3.3),

$$I = \mathscr{R}R^2.$$

The comparison with the sun then gives

$$\frac{I_*}{I_\odot} = \frac{\mathscr{R}_*}{\mathscr{R}_\odot}\left(\frac{R_*}{R_\odot}\right)^2 = \left(\frac{T_{e*}}{T_{e\odot}}\right)^4\left(\frac{R_*}{R_\odot}\right)^2.$$

Further, by taking logarithms and introducing absolute bolometric magnitudes M_b, we obtain

$$\log\left(T_{e*}/T_{e\odot}\right) = -0.1(M_{b*} - M_{b\odot}) - 0.5\log\left(R_*/R_\odot\right).$$

With

$$M_{b\odot} = 4.78, \qquad T_{e\odot} = 5800°\ \mathrm{K},$$

$$\log T_{e*} = 4.241 - 0.1M_{b*} - 0.5\log\left(R_*/R_\odot\right). \qquad (61.4)$$

This relation can serve for evaluating the effective temperatures of eclipsing stars for which the ratio $R_*/R_\odot$ has been determined, providing their absolute magnitudes are known.

For the stars of B3 V, whose absolute photovisual magnitude is about $M_{pv} = -1.8$, the bolometric correction is about $BC = -1.9$ (Table I, § 22). We therefore take $M_b = -3.7$. The study of eclipsing systems (Table VI, § 66) leads further to $R_*/R_\odot = 4.5$, from which $T_e = 19,230°\ \mathrm{K}$.

For the subgiant β Aur (A1 IV): $R_*/R_\odot = 2.7$, $M_{pv} = +0.66$, $BC = -0.50$ magnitude, from which $T_e = 10,200°\ \mathrm{K}$.

For Castor C (K7 V), of the α Gem system, we find $R_*/R_\odot = 0.635$, $M_{pv} = 9.0$, $BC = -1.4$ magnitude, from which $T_e = 3800°\ \mathrm{K}$.

On the graph of Figure 28, relating to color temperatures (§ 48), the crosses represent the effective temperatures of the sun and the stars calculated above. There does not appear to be any marked difference between the two types of temperature in the case of red dwarfs (K).

But, for hotter stars, the effective temperature seems systematically lower than the color temperature measured in the blue-violet region ($T_e = 19,200°$ K, $T_c = 24,600°$ K for the B3 V stars).

It is necessary not to lose sight of the fact that the color temperature generally differs according to the spectral region studied. In the case of the sun, for example, where rather precise measurements are available, it is about 7540° K *at the center of the disk* for the wavelength interval 3700–4900 A (Labs 1957).[1] The color temperature relative to radiation from the entire disk is lower, but shows analogous variations. Even higher than 6000° K in the blue and visible regions, it can be in the vicinity of 5000° K between 3400 and 2200 A according to spectrograms obtained with rockets.

[1] Translator's note: According to Labs' more recent data (1962), the color temperatures are somewhat lower than this, closer to the values of 7150° and 5780° K given earlier by Minnaert (1953).

CHAPTER IX

MASSES AND DENSITIES OF STARS

All of the knowledge acquired about the masses of stars arises from the extension to double stars of Newton's law of gravitation, which is verified in the solar system. We do not propose in this chapter to study the realm of double stars for its own sake, but only to show how the study of these objects informs us of the masses and sometimes of the densities of stars.

The investigation of visual binaries is traditionally associated with positional astronomy [8, 26]. On the other hand, the study of *spectroscopic* and *photometric* binaries depends on the customary techniques of astrophysics.

62. Information furnished by visual binaries

Repeated over a sufficiently long time—because the periods of visual binaries are counted ordinarily in decades or centuries—the measurements of the relative position of a component B of a binary system with respect to the other component A (distance and position angle) allow the drawing of an *apparent* orbit of B with respect to A. This is the projection of the *relative* orbit of B with respect to A onto the plane tangent to the celestial sphere. The knowledge of the apparent orbit and the epoch corresponding to the observed positions leads to the determination of the relative orbit in space [8, 26]. We find:

—the angular value α of the semi-major axis a of the ellipse,

—the eccentricity $e = c/a$ (c is the distance from the center of the ellipse to a focus),

—the inclination $\pm i$ of the orbital plane on the plane tangent to the celestial sphere, of indeterminate sign, because two planes symmetrical with respect to the tangent plane and having the same intersection with it obviously give in projection the same apparent orbit.

When we know in addition the distance of the system from the sun, we also obtain:

—the linear value of the semi-major axis $a = r\alpha$ (α in radians),

—the sum of the masses $\mathfrak{M}_1 + \mathfrak{M}_2$ of the two stars.

The third law of Kepler can be written as

$$\frac{a^3}{P^2} = \frac{G}{4\pi^2} (\mathfrak{M}_1 + \mathfrak{M}_2),$$

where P is the period of revolution and G the constant of universal gravitation. Let us take as the unit of length the semi-major axis of the terrestrial orbit, as the unit of time the sidereal year, and as the unit of mass the mass of the sun. The same law applied to the earth–sun pair, where the mass of the earth is negligible with respect to the sun, gives

$$1 = \frac{G}{4\pi^2}$$

from which, with the chosen units,

$$\frac{a^3}{P^2} = \mathfrak{M}_1 + \mathfrak{M}_2. \tag{62.1}$$

With photography, by means of a long-focus refractor, we can measure the displacements of each of the two components with respect to a group of field stars, following the technique used for the measurement of parallaxes. In this way we determine not just the relative orbit, but the orbits of each of the two stars around the center of gravity of the system. Its position is defined by

$$\mathfrak{M}_1 a_1 = \mathfrak{M}_2 a_2, \tag{62.2}$$

a_1 and a_2 being the semi-major axes of the two ellipses that are measured. Then we deduce the ratio of masses and, finally, the individual masses. If the parallax is unknown, we only get the angular values α_1 and α_2 of the semi-major axes and the ratio of masses.

63. Spectroscopic binary stars

A star which appears single in a telescope sometimes shows in its spectrum two distinct systems of lines that oscillate with identical periods but with unequal amplitudes on both sides of a mean position. At each instant the systems have opposite phases. It is natural to interpret the oscillations of the lines as the periodic variations in radial velocity of two stars in orbital movement. They form a pair too close to be resolved with a telescope.

Even more frequently the star shows only one system of periodically oscillating lines. The same explanation in general prevails, although one component has too little luminosity for its lines to be perceptible.

By placing on the abscissa the phases $\varphi = 2\pi t/P$, on the ordinates the radial velocities of one component, we obtain a curve whose form depends essentially on the eccentricity of the orbit and orientation of the line of apsides with respect to the line of sight [4]. The orbital radial velocity can be cast into the form

$$v_z = \frac{na_1 \sin i}{\sqrt{1 - e^2}} \, (e \cos \omega + u), \qquad (63.1)$$

where n is the mean angular motion $2\pi/P$,

     a_1 the semi-major axis of the ellipse described by the first component around the center of gravity,

     e the eccentricity,

     i the inclination of the orbital plane with respect to the plane tangent to the sphere,

     ω the angle formed by the line of nodes of the two preceding planes and the line of apsides,

     u the angle formed at each instant by the radius vector and the line of nodes.

(See the derivation below.)

The period P being known from preliminary observations, the analysis of the radial velocity curve permits the determination of three parameters: e, which defines the form of the orbit; ω, which defines its orientation; and $a \sin i$, the projection of the semi-major axis on the line of sight. It is impossible to separate a and i by spectroscopic observations.

Derivation of the orbital radial velocity.—Let Ox be the line of nodes, the intersection of the orbital plane Π and the plane T tangent to the celestial sphere (Figs. 38 and 39), PP' the line of apsides, which makes the angle ω with Ox. The position of the star in M is, at each instant, defined by the angle $u = xOM$, computed in the direction of the motion, and the equation of the ellipse related to the axis Ox of the polar coordinates is

$$r = \frac{a_1(1 - e^2)}{1 + e \cos (u - \omega)}. \qquad (63.2)$$

The radius vector $r = OM$ has for its projection on the axis Oy in the plane of the orbit $y = r \sin u$, and its projection on the line of sight Oz is reduced to the projection of Oy, since Oz is normal to Ox.

$$z = y \sin i = r \sin u \sin i$$

$$= \frac{a_1(1 - e^2) \sin i \sin u}{1 + e \cos (u - \omega)}.$$

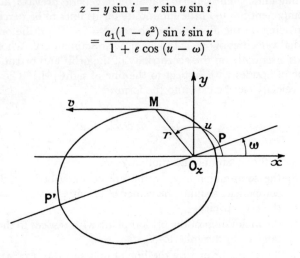

Fig. 38.

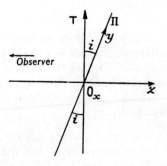

Fig. 39.

We obtain the orbital radial velocity $v_z = \mathrm{d}z/\mathrm{d}t$ by differentiating the preceding relation where u is the only function of time

$$\frac{\mathrm{d}z}{\mathrm{d}t} = \frac{a_1 \sin i (1 - e^2)(e \cos \omega + \cos u)}{[1 + e \cos (u - \omega)]^2} \frac{\mathrm{d}u}{\mathrm{d}t}. \tag{63.3}$$

$\mathrm{d}u/\mathrm{d}t$ can be evaluated by the law of areas

$$r^2 \frac{\mathrm{d}u}{\mathrm{d}t} = C = \frac{2\pi a_1^2}{P} \sqrt{1 - e^2} = na_1^2 \sqrt{1 - e^2}.$$

(The value of the constant C results from the fact that the area swept out in time P is that of the ellipse, that is, $\pi a_1^2 \sqrt{1 - e^2}$.)

By placing this value of $\mathrm{d}u/\mathrm{d}t$ in (63.3) and by replacing r by its expression (63.2), we obtain the formula (63.1).

To the orbital radial velocity v_z must, of course, be added the radial velocity V_0 of translation of the system with respect to the sun. The measured heliocentric radial velocity (after correction for the motion of the observer with respect to the sun) is thus

$$V_z = V_0 + v_z,$$

but V_0 is easily determined by noting that the integral $\int_t^{t+P} v_z \, \mathrm{d}t$, taken over an entire period, must vanish. The position of the ordinate V_0 is thus such that the areas 1 and 2 are equal (Fig. 40).

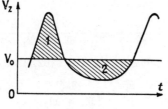

Fig. 40.

INFORMATION OBTAINED ABOUT MASSES.—Two cases will be considered depending on whether two components or a single one are observed in the spectra.

First case.—When we can construct both radial velocity curves, we obtain separately the products $\mathfrak{M}_1 \sin^3 i$ and $\mathfrak{M}_2 \sin^3 i$, from which the ratio of the masses follows.

The position of the system's center of gravity is defined by (62.2) and the third law of Kepler is expressed by (62.1), with the above-mentioned choice of units. The elimination of $\mathfrak{M}_2$ between the two equations gives

$$\mathfrak{M}_1 = \frac{a^3}{P^2 \left(1 + \dfrac{a_1}{a_2}\right)}. \tag{63.4}$$

We do not know a, but we have the products $a_1 \sin i$ and $a_2 \sin i$, from which

$$a \sin i = a_1 \sin i + a_2 \sin i.$$

Multiplying the two members of (63.4) by $\sin^3 i$, we find

$$\mathfrak{M}_1 \sin^3 i = \frac{(a \sin i)^3}{P^2 \left(1 + \dfrac{a_1 \sin i}{a_2 \sin i}\right)}.$$

The right side of this relation includes only known quantities. Thus we can calculate $\mathfrak{M}_1 \sin^3 i$. Similarly we could calculate $\mathfrak{M}_2 \sin^3 i$ by eliminating $\mathfrak{M}_1$ instead of $\mathfrak{M}_2$ between (62.1) and (62.2).

Second case.—When only one radial velocity curve is available, we obtain only a certain *mass function*, which is written

$$f(\mathfrak{M}_1, \mathfrak{M}_2) = \frac{(\mathfrak{M}_2 \sin i)^3}{(\mathfrak{M}_1 + \mathfrak{M}_2)^2}.$$

The index 1 is assigned to the star whose spectrum is observed. We have thus determined $a_1 \sin i$ but not $a_2 \sin i$. The relation (62.2) gives

$$\frac{a_1}{\mathfrak{M}_2} = \frac{a_2}{\mathfrak{M}_1} = \frac{a_1 + a_2}{\mathfrak{M}_1 + \mathfrak{M}_2} = \frac{a}{\mathfrak{M}_1 + \mathfrak{M}_2}. \qquad (63.5)$$

By eliminating a between (63.5) and (62.1) we obtain

$$\frac{a_1^3}{P^2} = \frac{\mathfrak{M}_2^3}{(\mathfrak{M}_1 + \mathfrak{M}_2)^2}.$$

Again multiplying each side by $\sin^3 i$, we have finally

$$\frac{(a_1 \sin i)^3}{P^2} = \frac{(\mathfrak{M}_2 \sin i)^3}{(\mathfrak{M}_1 + \mathfrak{M}_2)^2} = f(\mathfrak{M}_1, \mathfrak{M}_2),$$

where the left side is known. The mass function is thus determined.

RADIAL VELOCITIES OF VISUAL BINARIES.—It is rarely possible to measure the generally very small radial velocities of visual binaries. When they are available (ϵ Hyd, α Cen), we obtain the products $a_1 \sin i$ and $a_2 \sin i$. Since the drawing of the relative orbit gives i, the indeterminacy of the sign is cleared up and we can also evaluate a_1, a_2 and a. Moreover, the two radial velocity curves having revealed $\mathfrak{M}_1 \sin^3 i$ and $\mathfrak{M}_2 \sin^3 i$, we obtain the masses themselves. From the angular value α of the semi-major axis of the relative orbit and from its linear value a, we then derive the distance to the system.

64. Eclipsing binary stars. Light curves

The light of these photometric binary stars varies in a regular and periodic fashion: their *light curve*, which represents the magnitude or brightness variations as a function of time (or of phase $\varphi = 2\pi t/P$), is characterized by the existence of two minima per period, whose amplitudes can be quite different.

The study of radial velocities shows that they are spectroscopic binaries. The orbital radial velocity vanishes at the moments of minima: the trajectory of the stars is then perpendicular to the line of sight and the minima are explained as mutual eclipses of the two components. The eclipses are separated by exactly half the period when the relative orbit is circular, but are not equidistant when it is elliptic. In all cases the inclination i of the orbital plane is necessarily in the vicinity of 90°.

The periods of the eclipsing binaries are in the mean shorter than those of the other spectroscopic binaries: a small number of days or often a fraction of a day instead of several days or several tens of days. It is not necessary to propose a different nature for the two categories of stars. For a given value of the sum of the masses, the semi-major axis of the relative orbit becomes smaller as the period diminishes and the probability for the occurrence of eclipses increases for each inclination of the orbital plane.

The eclipsing stars are arranged into two principal groups according to the form of the light curve: the *Algol types* (Algol = β Per), whose luminosity variations outside of eclipse are very small, and the stars of the β *Lyrae type*, where these variations, much more important, round off the curve (the choice of β Lyr as the type star can nowadays be regretted, because it turns out to be a particularly complex system).

The light curve is most often established with photoelectric photometry, by taking one or more comparison stars in the immediate vicinity of the variable in such a manner as to reduce the corrections for atmospheric absorption. From a precise light curve one can find the following elements:

—B_1/B_2, the ratio of luminances of the two stars;
—R_1/a and R_2/a, the ratios of their radii to the radius a of the supposedly circular relative orbit;
—i, the inclination of the orbital plane.

The method of analysis of light curves, systematized by Russell, has been perfected by Russell and J. E. Merrill, Kopal, Zessewich, etc. Numerical tables and nomograms facilitate its application. We will try below to give a succinct idea without entering into the details of the always laborious calculations.

The variations observed outside the eclipse are explained by the *ellipticity* of the stars and by the *phase effect*. The two components are likened to ellipsoids of revolution, whose major axes turn constantly one toward the other. Their period of rotation (around the minor axis) is thus assumed equal to the period of revolution. The variations of the apparent surface of the ellipsoids will necessarily cause variations of light in the course of one revolution.

The phase effect arises from the fact that the two components mutually illuminate each other; the luminances of the sides facing each other are thereby increased. It is not a matter of a simple reflection, but a complex phenomenon of radiative transfer.

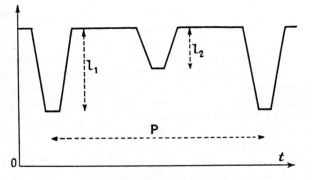

FIG. 41.   RECTIFIED LIGHT CURVE OF AN ECLIPSING VARIABLE.

The study of the variations outside of the eclipses permits us to take these two phenomena into account and to construct the so-called "rectified" light curve that would be observed in their absence. It is horizontal between eclipses (Fig. 41), and from this the photometric elements of the system are determined.

The rectified light is at each instant proportional to the luminous intensity L of the system. By taking as unity the intensity between eclipses we can write

$$B_1S_1 + B_2S_2 = 1$$

where S_1 and S_2 represent the apparent surfaces of the two stars.

Let us assume that the smaller star 1 has the greater luminosity (which is the most frequent case). It is then eclipsed at the principal minimum. Let f_0 be the fraction of the area S_1 eclipsed at the moment of this minimum. The *loss of light l* is then

$$l_1 = B_1 S_1 f_0.$$

At the moment of secondary minimum the larger star 2 is eclipsed by the smaller, but, on account of symmetry, the area of the eclipse is the same as at the principal minimum (Fig. 42); it is always $S_1 f_0$. The loss of light is thus

$$l_2 = B_2 S_1 f_0.$$

Dividing each side of these relations together, we obtain

$$l_1/l_2 = B_1/B_2. \qquad (64.1)$$

Principal min.

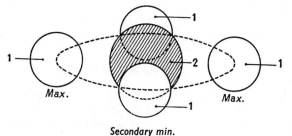

Max.

Secondary min.

Fig. 42.   Eclipsing binary system.

The ratio of the luminances is equal to the ratio of the loss of light in the two minima of the rectified curve.

In order to determine the other elements, let us assume that the eclipse of the small star is total at the principal minimum, which is then marked by a *constant phase* corresponding to the totality (Fig. 41). The loss of light l_1 is equal to the intensity L_1. The intensity of star 2 is in consequence $L_2 = 1 - l_1$, from which

$$L_1/L_2 = l_1/(1 - l_1)$$

and, by taking (64.1) into account,

$$\left(\frac{R_1}{R_2}\right)^2 = \frac{S_1}{S_2} = \frac{L_1 B_2}{L_2 B_1} = \frac{l_2}{1 - l_1}.$$

Thus the ratio $k = R_1/R_2$ of the two radii becomes known.

It remains to determine R_1/a and i. During the principal eclipse the light loss $1 - L$ is at each instant proportional to the fraction f of the eclipsed disk

$$1 - L = fL_1 = fl_1.$$

f is simultaneously a function of the already known ratio $k = R_1/R_2$ and of the ratio δ/R_1 where δ is the apparent distance of the centers of the two components, the projection of the radius a of the relative orbit on the plane normal to the line of sight. The ratio δ/a is easily expressed as a function of the inclination i of the orbital plane and the *phase angle* θ that is formed at each instant by the line of the centers with the projection of the visual radius on the orbital plane. This results in an equation containing the two unknowns R_1/a and i. It therefore suffices to choose two convenient values of θ (and thus of f) for the calculation.

When a constant phase is not observed at either of the two minima, we necessarily conclude that the two eclipses are partial ($f_0 < 1$). The knowledge of the light losses at the minima l_1 and l_2 is no longer sufficient for determining k and give only one relation between k and f_0. We find immediately

$$l_1 = L_1 f_0, \quad l_2 = L_2 k^2 f_0, \quad \text{from which} \quad f_0 = l_1 + l_2/k^2.$$

In order to have another relation between these two quantities it is necessary to consider the form of the light curve just before or after the principal minimum. The calculations are more complex and the results less certain.

The theory has been completed for adaptation to the case of elliptical orbits and that of stellar disks darkened toward the limb. When one eclipse is total, the other is necessarily annular: the darkening of the disk of the eclipsed star must then be marked by a continuous variation of light throughout the duration of the annular eclipse.

65. Combination of photometric and spectroscopic measurements

We obtain very complete information about the components of an eclipsing binary system when both spectra can be observed. The light curve and the two radial velocity curves lead in fact to an evaluation of the absolute dimensions of the two stars, their masses, and from this, their densities.

The light curve gives the inclination i of the orbital plane and the ratio of the radii of each component to the radius (or semi-major axis) of the relative orbit, R_1/a and R_2/a. The radial velocity curves, on the other hand, give the product $a \sin i$. We thus get in kilometers the radius a of the relative orbit and the radii R_1 and R_2 of the two components.

The radial velocity curves also reveal the products $\mathfrak{M}_1 \sin^3 i$ and $\mathfrak{M}_2 \sin^3 i$; $\sin i$ now having been determined, we obtain the masses $\mathfrak{M}_1$ and $\mathfrak{M}_2$. Knowing the masses and radii, we finally derive the densities ρ_1 and ρ_2.

The spectroscopic study of very close binaries has revealed in many cases unusual physical complications: the presence of a gaseous ring revolving rapidly around the two stars (RW Tau) or a gaseous envelope common to both components. Streams of gas sometimes manifest themselves between the stars (UX Mon, β Lyr). In the case of β Lyr, there also exists around the binary either an expanding gaseous ring or a spiral of gas ejected by one of the two stars (O. Struve, Kuiper) [30].

66. Collection of results concerning the masses and densities

The visual binaries of known parallax give information especially on the main sequence stars from class A to class M, which, for a given apparent brightness, are the nearest and therefore the most easily resolved. For a certain number of these we know the sum of the masses of the two components. An already rather old statistic, due to Aitken (1935), gives the mean value of the half-sum of the masses for various spectral classes:

Spectrum	B	B8–A3	A5–F3	F5–G2	G5–K2	M
$\frac{1}{2}(\mathfrak{M}_1 + \mathfrak{M}_2)$	5.32	2.01	1.30	1.21	1.07	0.31
N	1	21	11	37	16	2

(N is the number of binaries).

More recently van de Kamp [16] has collected the results relating to 12 binaries of well-known parallaxes and spectra, for which the masses of the two components could be determined separately. Of these, 15 belong to the main sequence. The logarithms of their masses are represented by circles on Figure 43.

The eclipsing binaries fortunately complete these data as far as hot stars are concerned, because the catalogued binaries, numbering more than 2000, show a very marked concentration in the classes B and A. This apparent distribution is in fact caused by selection: more luminous, the B and A stars can be detected at greater distances. Actually, in a limited volume around the sun, the largest number of eclipsing stars belong to the *W Ursae Majoris* type. These are dwarfs with a period less than one day usually belonging to classes F and G. Per unit volume their number seems 30 times greater than eclipsing binaries of classes A and B (Shapley, 1946).

S. Gaposchkin [16] has published a list of 81 eclipsing binary systems showing two spectra, for which the radii and masses have been well determined. In grouping by spectral types the results relative to the main sequence, we obtain the mean values of Table VI, represented graphically by the black points on Figure 43.

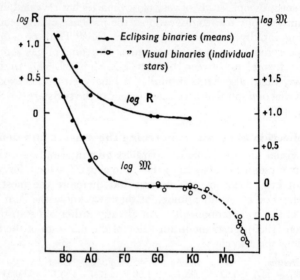

FIG. 43. VARIATION OF RADIUS AND MASS AS A FUNCTION OF SPECTRAL TYPE (MAIN SEQUENCE).

The mass diminishes very rapidly from the late O types to the late A types, then very slowly in classes F and G. The curve passes quite close to the individual points found from the study of visual binaries. The latter allow the extension of the curve to late M types. We observe there a new diminution of the mass, rapid on the red dwarf side. The means of Aitken for visual binaries would also lie very close to the curve.

The mean densities contained in the last column of the table have been calculated in g/cm³, by the formula $d = 1.41\mathfrak{M}/R^3$, the radii and masses being expressed in solar units. The density of the sun is 1.41 g/cm³.

Since the volume diminishes more quickly than the mass, the density increases constantly from O7 to K0, at first very quickly and then more slowly along the main sequence. Of the order of 0.1 g/cm³

TABLE VI

RADII, MASSES AND DENSITIES IN THE MAIN SEQUENCE

Spectra	N	$\bar{R}$ ($R_\odot = 1$)	$\overline{\mathfrak{M}}$ ($\mathfrak{M}_\odot = 1$)	$\bar{d}$ (g/cm³)
O7–O8	9	13.8	28.9	0.015
O9–B1	8	6.4	17.3	0.09
B3	18	4.5	7.9	0.12
B4–B9	14	2.8	4.7	0.29
A0	11	1.95	2.15	0.41
A2–A9	8	1.4	1.15	0.62
F8	4	0.94	0.91	1.29
F9–G3	15	0.89	0.91	1.82
G5–K2	9	0.88	0.88	1.83

N = number of components.

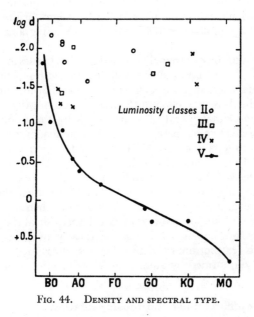

Fig. 44. Density and spectral type.

for the early B types, it reaches 1 g/cm³ in class F and approaches 2 g/cm³ in class K.

The data relative to giants are not extensive enough to allow the drawing of a mean curve. On Figure 44 we have plotted as a function of spectral type the logarithms of the mean densities of the dwarfs and of the individual densities of some typical giants and bright giants, calculated from quantities in the list by Gaposchkin. These densities lie in general between 0.008 and 0.03 g/cm^3. The appearance of the graph recalls that of the H-R diagram (§ 38).

For some supergiants we find much smaller densities still. The duration of the eclipse of the B component of the ζ Aur system by the K5 supergiant leads to the evaluation of the radius of this latter star at 245 solar radii. Its mass being in the vicinity of 16.4 $\odot$, its density must be about $1.6 \cdot 10^{-6}$ g/cm^3.

The ϵ Aur system contains an F supergiant that is totally eclipsed every 27 years by an enormous infrared star. Their radii are evaluated at 716 and 1278 solar radii, respectively, with masses of 42 and 28 $\odot$. The corresponding densities would therefore be $1.6 \cdot 10^{-7}$ and $1.9 \cdot 10^{-8}$ g/cm^3. Finally, VV Cep includes a B8 star ($R = 19.4$ $\odot$) and an enormous red supergiant M2 Ia, whose radius extends to 1940 $\odot$. We attribute to each of the two components the same mass of 24.2 $\odot$, which yields densities of $1.9 \cdot 10^{-3}$ g/cm^3 for the blue giant and 5.10^{-9} g/cm^3 for the red supergiant (5 milligrams per cubic meter).

In contrast to these extremely rarefied gaseous masses are found the *white dwarfs*, whose masses can be well determined from stars that are part of a binary system, such as the companions of Sirius and Procyon. That of Sirius B is very close to the mass of the sun ($\mathfrak{M} = 0.98$ $\odot$). We can approximately calculate its radius by the formula (61.4), knowing its effective temperature and absolute magnitude. The A5 spectrum leads to taking $T_e = 8700°$ K and the bolometric correction BC $= -0.34$ magnitude (Table I, § 22). From the apparent visual magnitude $m_v = 8.64$ and its parallax $p = 0''.379$, we further derive the absolute visual magnitude $M_v = 11.53$, and then the absolute bolometric magnitude $M_b = 11.19$. The formula then gives $R_*/R_\odot = 0.023$ ($\simeq 1.6 \cdot 10^4$ km, or about 2.5 times the terrestrial radius). The density therefore equals $1.1 \cdot 10^5$ g/cm^3 (nearly two tons per cubic inch). This extraordinary density corresponds to a completely degenerate gas, formed by atomic nuclei stripped of their retinue of electrons.

67. The empirical mass-luminosity relation

The preceding results suggest the existence of a relation (at least statistically) between the masses and luminosities of stars, a relation furthermore justified by the theoretical researches of Eddington on the internal constitution of the stars. One is led to represent the absolute bolometric magnitude M_b by a linear function of the logarithm of the mass $\mathfrak{M}$ (expressed in solar masses)

$$M_b = \log A - B \log \mathfrak{M}.$$

This is equivalent to writing the luminosity L of the star as

$$L = a\mathfrak{M}^p.$$

We generally evaluate L by taking the luminosity of the sun as unity. We then have

$$\log a = 0.4(M_{b\odot} - \log A), \quad p = 0.4B.$$

Table VII groups together the values of the coefficient a and the exponent p obtained by various authors, by reducing $M_{b\odot}$ in all cases to $M_{b\odot} = 4.79$.

TABLE VII

MASS-LUMINOSITY RELATION

Authority	a	p	
Parenago (1937)	0.87	3.35	$0.2 < \mathfrak{M} < 50$ visual, spectroscopic and eclipsing binaries.
Kuiper (1938)	1.17	3.5	$0.3 < \mathfrak{M} < 4$ visual, spectroscopic and eclipsing binaries.
Russell and Moore (1940)	0.67	3.82	Main sequence (a more complex relation for the group of stars).
Parenago and Massevich (1950)	$\begin{cases} 1.06 \\ 0.38 \end{cases}$	$\begin{matrix} 3.92 \\ 2.29 \end{matrix}$	$1 < \mathfrak{M} < 20$ visual, spectroscopic and eclipsing binaries. $\mathfrak{M} < 1$, red dwarfs.
van de Kamp (1954)	$\begin{cases} 1.05 \\ 0.33 \end{cases}$	$\begin{matrix} 4 \\ 2 \end{matrix}$	$0.6 < \mathfrak{M} < 2.5$ visual binaries. $\mathfrak{M} < 1$, red dwarfs.
Eggen (1956)	1.0	3.1	$0.6 < \mathfrak{M} < 2.5$ visual binaries.

The obvious differences between these results arise in large part from the uncertainty of the masses and the absolute bolometric magnitudes. The researches of Parenago, Russell and Moore, and Parenago and Massevich recommend themselves by the abundance of sources used, those of Eggen by their homogeneity. Eggen has in fact determined the absolute magnitudes by means of the relation established for single stars of the main sequence between M_v and the

Masses and densities of stars

photoelectric color index measured with a blue filter and a yellow filter.   Figure 45 represents the line drawn by Eggen,

$$M_b = 4.79 - 7.8 \log \mathfrak{M}.$$

Eggen has also discussed the case of a certain number of giants and subgiants, which, as a whole, seem to satisfy the same relation.

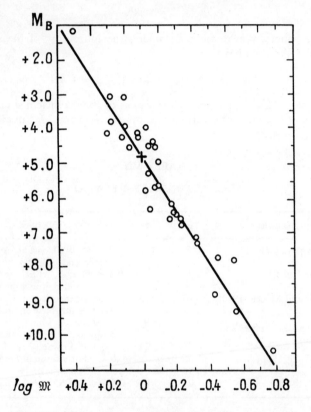

FIG. 45.   MASS-LUMINOSITY RELATION (according to EGGEN).

It is not certain, however, that all the stars taken together verify a unique relation.   Thus for the stars of mass $\mathfrak{M} > 1$, we find a coefficient a near unity and an exponent p falling between 3.1 and 3.9, whereas the red dwarfs ($\mathfrak{M} < 1$) seem to lead to a clearly smaller value of a and an exponent little greater than 2 (Parenago and Massevich, van de Kamp).

Departures from the law.—In addition to the white dwarfs, excluded *a priori* by Eddington's theory, which do not agree at all with the mass-luminosity relation, we find some notable deviations.

Petrie evaluated the difference ΔM in the absolute magnitudes of the two components of spectroscopic binaries from the intensity of the lines in the two spectra (64 binaries studied). In 90% of the cases this difference conforms to the law, but when the masses of the components are much different, at least one of the stars is too luminous.

The fainter component of an eclipsing binary agrees much less well with the law than the bright component when its mass or its density is very different from that of the principal star. The less massive or less dense star is too luminous for its mass. The two components of W *Ursae Majoris* agree rather badly with the law, just as does the faint component of Algol types, whose mass is often abnormally small.

Some much more important deviations have been discovered: thus the luminosity of the weak components of the systems XZ Sag and R CMa seem more than 1000 times lower than the predicted value (O. Struve). In the case of very close binaries (β *Lyrae* and W UMa types) the deviations must be related to the fact that the two components are almost in contact and are surrounded by a common envelope (§ 65). When it is a question of rather distant pairs the deviations could indicate a difference in their present chemical composition, probably resulting from a more rapid evolution of one of the components (§ 78).

Application: dynamic parallaxes of double stars.—Kepler's third law, which is used for evaluating the sum of the masses of a visual binary system of known parallax (§ 62), can be used inversely to calculate the parallax p when the sum of the masses is known. We have measured the angular value α of the semi-major axis, which equals in radians $\alpha = a/r$. Also in radians, $p = 1/r$, whence $a = \alpha/p$, a valid relation independent of the angular units chosen. Using this relation to eliminate a from Kepler's third law (62.1), we obtain

$$p = \alpha/a = \alpha P^{-2/3}(\mathfrak{M}_1 + \mathfrak{M}_2)^{-1/3}.$$

The parallax is inversely proportional to the cube root of the sum of the masses. The relative error in p is therefore three times smaller than in $\mathfrak{M}_1 + \mathfrak{M}_2$ and the parallax so found is rather well determined even when the sum of the masses is known only in an approximate manner.

The masses vary only within narrow limits along the main sequence between types A5 and K0 (Fig. 43). For a long time astronomers were content to take $\mathfrak{M}_1 + \mathfrak{M}_2 = 2$ regardless of spectral type. The mass-luminosity relation and the mass-spectral type relation furnish a more satisfactory solution, by successive approximations. We first choose an initial value approaching $\mathfrak{M}_1 + \mathfrak{M}_2$ according to the spectral types of the components. The parallax obtained allows the evaluation of the absolute bolometric magnitudes, and the mass-luminosity relation leads to a new evaluation of $\mathfrak{M}_1 + \mathfrak{M}_2$, from which a new value of the parallax follows, etc. (Russell and Moore).

CHAPTER X

ELEMENTARY IDEAS ON THE CONSTITUTION OF STELLAR ATMOSPHERES

68. The atmospheres of stars

At the beginning of the twentieth century it was thought that the continuous spectrum of a star was emitted from a layer of determined temperature, the *photosphere*, overlaid by an absorbing layer responsible for the absorption lines. The properties of the photosphere in thermo-dynamic equilibrium could then be characterized by temperature alone, its continuous spectrum resembling that of a black body.

Actually the radiation always differs more or less from that of a black body (§ 48), because it is emitted from various depths, so that today we designate as the stellar atmosphere the group of layers from which the observed radiation arises: the continuous spectrum having absorption lines and, possibly, emission lines.

To what extent do these observations inform us about the con-stitution of stellar atmospheres? It is this question that we shall try to answer in this chapter, without entering into the details of a complex theory, which would be out of place in an elementary work.

We consider the stars as gaseous masses, whose very dense and hot central region is the seat of nuclear reactions, the source of the radiant energy. It is possible that in certain layers convective energy trans-port plays an important role, but, as a whole, the transfer of energy from one volume element to another in the star operates essentially by means of radiation (*radiative equilibrium*). We further assume (which is certainly not true in all cases) that thermodynamic equilibrium is *locally* achieved in each thin layer (Milne). This means that Kirch-hoff's law holds at each point: the ratio between the *emission coefficient* j_λ and the *absorption coefficient* k_λ for the same wavelength is then given by Planck's law.[1] Moreover, the distribution of the velocities of the

---

[1] j_λ is the energy radiated by a volume element of unit cross section and length ds, in the small solid angle $d\omega$ with axis parallel to ds, between the wavelengths λ and $\lambda + \Delta\lambda$. The ratio j_λ/k_λ equals the spectral brilliance b_λ of a black body, which is obtained by dividing π into the spectral radiance ρ_λ given by formula (46.1).

particles is governed by Maxwell's law. But since the temperature varies with depth, the radiation leaving the star does not correspond in its entirety to that of a black body.

69. Excitation and ionization

Boltzmann equation.—Radiative equilibrium having supposedly been established, the number N of atoms or ions of an element present at each energy level, as well as the number of free electrons, can be considered as a steady state $(\mathrm{d}N/\mathrm{d}t = 0)$. Quantum mechanics shows that, if local thermodynamic equilibrium is also established, the distribution of atoms or ions in the various energy levels is represented as a function of the absolute temperature T by the Boltzmann formula

$$\frac{N_b}{N_a} = \frac{g_b}{g_a}\, e^{-(\chi_{ab}/kT)}. \tag{69.1}$$

N_a and N_b are the numbers of atoms present per unit volume at the energy levels a and b (b above a), χ_{ab} is the energy difference of the two levels, k the Boltzmann constant. Finally, g_a and g_b are the *statistical weights* of the levels a and b. If J represents the total angular momentum of the atom, calculable for each known level, $g = 2\mathrm{J} + 1$. In the particular case of the hydrogen atom, for the orbital level m, $g_m = 2m^2$.

By calculating with (69.1) the ratio N_i/N_1 relative to each excited level, numbered 2, 3, etc., and the fundamental level 1, N_i is easily related to the total number N of atoms existing in a given state of ionization

$$N = N_1 + N_2 + \cdots$$

$$= \frac{N_1}{g_1}\, (g_1 + g_2\, e^{-(\chi_2/kT)} + g_3\, e^{-(\chi_3/kT)} + \cdots). \tag{69.2}$$

The sum of the terms between parentheses is called the *partition function*

$$u(T) = \Sigma\, g_i\, e^{-(\chi_i/kT)}$$

and can in principle be calculated for each temperature, if the statistical weights of the different levels are known.[2]

---

[2] When the second level possesses an energy greater than 1 eV above the fundamental level—a very frequent case—in replacing $u(T)$ by the statistical weight g_1 of the fundamental level one commits an error of less than 1% for $T \simeq 5000°$ K and 2% for $T \simeq 10,000°$ K.

With this notation the relation (69.2) becomes

$$N_1/N = g_1/u(T)$$

and, by combining it with equation (69.1), we obtain

$$\frac{N_i}{N} = \frac{g_i}{u(T)} \, e^{-(\chi_i/kT)}, \tag{69.3}$$

which is the most common form of the Boltzmann equation.

In numerical calculations it is convenient to use base-10 logarithms and to express the excitation energies in electron volts rather than ergs. One electron volt equals $1.602 \cdot 10^{-12}$ ergs.[3]

Then if E is the excitation energy in eV:

$$\log_{10} \left(e^{-(\chi/kT)\text{ergs}} \right) = -\log_{10} e \, \frac{1.602 \cdot 10^{-12}}{1.3803 \cdot 10^{-16}} \frac{E}{T} = -\frac{5040}{T} E$$

and formulas (69.1) and (69.3) become

$$\log \frac{N_b}{N_a} = -\frac{5040}{T} E + \log \frac{g_b}{g_a}, \tag{69.4}$$

$$\log \frac{N_i}{N} = -\frac{5040}{T} E + \log \frac{g_i}{u(T)}. \tag{69.5}$$

Saha equation.—By applying the laws of chemical equilibrium to the ionization of an atom

$$A \rightleftharpoons A^+ + e^-,$$

Saha has expressed, as a function of the absolute temperature and pressure P_e exerted by the free electrons, the ratio N_{r+1}/N_r between the numbers of atoms per unit volume $r + 1$ times and r times ionized (1921),[4]

$$\frac{N_{r+1}}{N_r} P_e = 2 \, \frac{u_{r+1}}{u_r} \frac{(2\pi m_e)^{3/2}}{h^3} \, (kT)^{5/2} \, e^{-(\chi_r/kT)}. \tag{69.6}$$

χ_r is the ionization energy of the atom already r times ionized, h and k the Planck and Boltzmann constants, m_e the mass of the electron,

---

[3] This is the energy acquired by the charge ϵ of the electron ($4.806 \cdot 10^{-10}$ E.S.U.) when it goes through a potential drop of 1 volt (1/300 E.S.U.). It follows that

$$1 \text{ eV} = 4.806 \cdot 10^{-10}/300 = 1.602 \cdot 10^{-12} \text{ ergs.}$$

[4] A more rigorous demonstration has been given by Fowler and Milne (1923); in [1] is found a simplified form due to Menzel.

u_{r+1} and u_r the partition functions of the atoms $r + 1$ and r times ionized.

When we substitute for the ionization energy χ_r in ergs its value I_r in eV and then replace the constants by their numerical values, we obtain by taking base-10 logarithms

$$\log \frac{N_{r+1}}{N_r} = -\frac{5040}{T} I_r + 2.5 \log T - 0.48 + \log \left(\frac{2u_{r+1}}{u_r}\right) - \log P_e.$$
(69.7)

70. Electron pressure and gas pressure

Let $\mathfrak{N}_0$ be the number per cm³ of atoms of all kinds, neutral or ionized. The perfect gas law, applied successively to free electrons and to the ensemble of all particles, gives

$$P_e = N_e kT, \qquad P_g = (\mathfrak{N}_0 + N_e)kT,$$

whence the ratio between gas pressure P_g and electron pressure P_e:

$$P_g/P_e = 1 + \mathfrak{N}_0/N_e.$$

The preponderance of hydrogen, which furnishes a single electron per atom, allows us to neglect the twice-ionized atoms. The number of free electrons is then equal to the sum of the number of ions of each kind:

$$N_e = N_1^+ + N_2^+ + \cdots.$$

The number of all neutral or ionized atoms is

$$\mathfrak{N}_0 = N_1 + N_1^+ + N_2 + N_2^+ + \cdots.$$

In the hot stars where just helium is in general only partially ionized, $\mathfrak{N}_0/N_e$ is little higher than 1 and P_g/P_e is little higher than 2. In atmospheres of cooler stars, such as the sun, hydrogen, almost entirely in a neutral state, is still responsible for the largest part of the gas pressure, but the electron pressure is provided only by the easily ionized metals. The ratio P_g/P_e becomes very large and, in order to calculate it, we must know approximately the chemical composition (§ 75).

If we know also the ionization energy of each element and choose an appropriate value for the electron pressure, we can calculate successively with the Saha equation the ratios N_1^+/N_1, N_2^+/N_2, ..., and finally $\mathfrak{N}_0/N_e$.

It is convenient to group the atoms of low abundance whose ionization energies are close to one another. Aller [1] considers four groups and, with the electron pressure $P_e = 100$ baryes $= 100$ dynes/cm^2, obtains for $T = 12,600°$ K and for $T = 6300°$ K the numbers contained in Table VIII. At 6300° K the ratio P_g/P_e is about 1000 times greater than at 12,600° K.

TABLE VIII

Group	Elements	I(eV)	$N + N^+$	N^+/N	
				12,600° K	6300° K
1	He	24.5	200	0.04	0
2	H	13.54	1000	1.00	0.00016
3	Fe, Si, Mg, Ni	7.9	0.43	1.00	0.835
4	Al, Ca, Na	5.8	0.011	1.00	1.00
	P_g/P_e			2.2	2274

71. Applications to spectral classification

According to the Boltzmann formula the distribution of atoms in the excited levels depends exclusively on the temperature, but the degree of ionization depends also on the pressure (Saha equation).

As a first approximation we can assume that in the spectral type where a line shows its maximum intensity the number of *absorbing* atoms is also at its maximum. The Boltzmann and Saha formulas then allow the calculation of the temperature of the stellar atmosphere, if we are given the electron pressure. For each value of P_e there will correspond a different scale of *excitation temperatures*.

Fowler and Milne (1923) have shown that we obtain a probable scale by adopting uniformly in all the spectral types of the main sequence $P_e = 130$ baryes ($1.3 \cdot 10^{-4}$ atmosphere):

B0 25,000° K, B2 16,000, A0 10,000

G5 5000, K5 4000° K.

(We thus obtain for the first time the temperatures corresponding to the early B types.)

We know today that the electron pressure is actually smaller in the cool stars (less than 10 baryes below 5000° K), greater in the hot stars (of the order of 200 baryes in type A0). But, within these limits, the electron pressure influences the ionization much less than the temperature does, and we shall retain as a first approximation the value $P_e = 130$ baryes to study in two examples the intensity variations of the lines along the main sequence, even though it is only a mean value corresponding approximately to dwarf stars whose effective temperature is in the vicinity of 7600° K.

FIRST EXAMPLE: THE BALMER LINES.—The Balmer lines are absorbed from the second energy level of the hydrogen atom. We calculate with the Boltzmann formula (69.4) the ratio N_2/N_1 of atoms in the level 2 with respect to the fundamental level 1. The excitation energy 2 is $E = 10.15$ eV; $g_1 = 2$, $g_2 = 2 \times 2^2 = 8$, from which

$$\log \frac{N_2}{N_1} = -\frac{5040}{T} \times 10.15 + \log 4.$$

By constructing the curve $\log (N_2/N_1) = f(T)$, we establish that N_2/N_1 passes from $1.2 \cdot 10^{-8}$ at 6000° K to $3 \cdot 10^{-5}$ at 10,000° K and $7.9 \cdot 10^{-2}$ at 30,000° K. Since N_2 is always much smaller than N_1, the ratio N_2/N_1 is practically equal to the ratio N_2/N, the number of absorbing atoms to the total number of neutral atoms. (The lines of the Lyman series, absorbed from level 1, are thus always much more intense than the Balmer lines, especially at low temperatures.)

But, as the temperature rises, the fraction of ionized atoms increases. Let us calculate the ratio N^+/N of the number of ionized to the number of neutral atoms. The ionization energy is $I = 13.54$ eV and $\log (2u^+/u) = 0$. With $P_e = 130$ baryes, the Saha formula (69.7) can be written

$$\log \frac{N^+}{N} = -\frac{5040}{T} \times 13.54 + 2.5 \log T - 2.59.$$

The increase of N^+/N as a function of the temperature is still more rapid than that of N_2/N_1: we find $N^+/N = 3.0 \cdot 10^{-5}$ at 6000° K, $3.8 \cdot 10^3$ at 10,000° K, $2.1 \cdot 10^6$ at 30,000° K.

Using the preceding results we easily evaluate the ratio $N_2/\mathfrak{N}$ of atoms absorbing the Balmer lines to the total number of neutral and ionized atoms $\mathfrak{N} = N + N^+$:

$$\frac{N_2}{\mathfrak{N}} = \frac{N_2}{N + N^+} = \frac{N_2/N}{1 + N^+/N}.$$

Figure 46 shows that the ratio $N_2/\mathfrak{N}$ increases very quickly from 6000 to 10,000° K, where it passes a maximum, and then diminishes more slowly toward the higher temperatures. The Balmer lines show the greatest intensity in the A0 stars. In their atmospheres the temperature must thus be in the vicinity of 10,000° K. The appearance of the curve also explains why the intensity of the Balmer lines diminishes more slowly in the hotter stars (classes B and O) than in the cooler stars (classes F and G). The increase in electron pressure in the stars of high temperature further accentuates this asymmetry by retarding the diminution of intensity of lines toward the high temperatures.

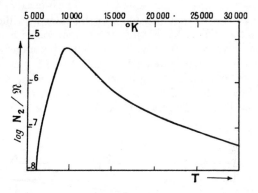

Fig. 46. Balmer lines. Ratio of the number of absorbing atoms to the total number of hydrogen atoms, from 5000 to 30,000° K.

Second example: resonance lines of Ca and Ca⁺.—This time it is necessary to study the equilibrium between Ca atoms and the ions Ca^+ and Ca^{++} by means of the Saha equation. We shall again take $P_e = 130$ baryes ($\log P_e = 2.11$). For the Ca atom, $I = 6.09$ eV, $\log (2u^+/u) = 0.44$; for the Ca^+ ion, $I = 11.87$ eV, $\log (2u^{++}/u^+) = -0.25$. By applying (69.7) we obtain

$$\log (N^+/N) = -\frac{5040}{T} \times 6.09 + 2.5 \log T - 2.15$$

$$\log (N^{++}/N) = -\frac{5040}{T} \times 17.96 + 5 \log T - 4.99.$$

If $\mathfrak{R}$ represents the total number of neutral and once or twice ionized calcium atoms,

$$\frac{N}{\mathfrak{R}} = \frac{1}{1 + N^+/N + N^{++}/N} = \frac{1}{A}, \qquad \frac{N^+}{\mathfrak{R}} = \frac{N^+}{N} \times \frac{1}{A},$$

$$\frac{N^{++}}{\mathfrak{R}} = \frac{N^{++}}{N} \times \frac{1}{A}.$$

Figure 47 shows the variations of the logarithms of these three ratios between 3000 and 15,000° K. At high temperatures practically all the calcium is found in the twice-ionized state Ca^{++}, whose lines fall in an unobservable ultraviolet region. Below 15,000° K the number of Ca^+ ions becomes appreciable and the *H* and *K* lines begin to appear in types B3–B5. Between 7500 and 5000° K almost all the calcium is in the singly ionized state Ca^+. The intensity of the *H* and *K* lines ought thus to be a maximum in this interval, which includes solar-type stars (class G). Finally, the proportion of neutral atoms increases rapidly below 5000° K, the ionization becoming almost zero below 3000° K. The resonance line 4227 A of Ca I must therefore become more and more strengthened in stars of low temperature. We have thus qualitatively accounted for the intensity variations in the resonance lines of Ca II and Ca I along the spectral series.[5]

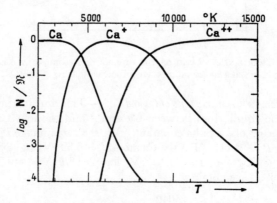

Fig. 47. Ratio of the number of neutral Ca atoms, Ca^+ and Ca^{++} ions to the total number of calcium atoms, from 2000 to 15,000° K.

The discussion is incomplete because it is based on the total number of atoms and ions, while only the population of the fundamental levels absorbs the resonance lines. Toward the high temperatures, the progressive populating of the excited levels tends to weaken the resonance lines more rapidly, but it appears futile to

[5] Figure 20 (§ 35) shows that the intensity maxima of the Sr II resonance lines ($I = 5.67$ eV) and the 4325 line of Fe I ($E = 1.60$ eV) are found in neighboring spectral types. The calculation accounts rather well for this apparently paradoxical fact. With $P_e = 10$ baryes we find that the broad maximum for Sr II corresponds to $T \simeq 5000$ to 5500° K (type G8 or G5) and the narrower maximum of Fe I 4325 corresponds to $T \simeq 4500°$ K (type K0).

attempt a higher degree of approximation while retaining the hypothesis of a constant electron pressure.

72. Spectral differences between giants and dwarfs

The theory of ionization explains the intensity difference in the lines of neutral and ionized atoms in the giants and dwarfs (§ 36). In the atmosphere of a giant the electron pressure is in fact, like the gas pressure, much smaller than in the atmosphere of a dwarf of the same temperature, and according to Saha's formula an abatement of electron pressure favors ionization.

First example (taken from Aller [1]).—Let us compare the ionization of iron and of calcium in a giant and a dwarf of type M2 having essentially the same temperature, 3150° K. For the dwarf we shall take $P_e = 2.5$ baryes, for the giant $P_e = 0.1$ barye.

In the case of iron ($I = 7.86$ eV, log $(2u^+/u) = 0.40$), the formula (69.7) gives, for the dwarf $N^+/N = 4.9 \cdot 10^{-5}$, for the giant $N^+/N = 1.2 \cdot 10^{-3}$. Even though the ionization is more pronounced in the giant, iron can be considered for practical purposes as neutral in the atmospheres of the two stars.

In the case of calcium, with the numerical data of § 71, we find for the dwarf $N^+/N = 0.036$, for the giant $N^+/N = 0.912$. The proportion of ionized atoms is notable in the two stars, but 25 times smaller in the dwarf. We notice that in this latter star the 4227 line of neutral calcium is much stronger.

Second example (inspired by Aller).—Let us now consider two G5 stars, a dwarf of temperature 5520° K where the electron pressure is $P_e = 20$ baryes, and a giant of temperature a little lower than $T = 4650°$ K (§ 48) where the electron pressure is unknown.

Since the Fe I lines have the same appearance in the two spectra, we can assume that the ionization of iron is the same in the two stars and that the electron pressure can be derived for the giant. The Saha equation applied to the dwarf (with the numerical data of the preceding example) gives log $(N^+/N) = 0.80$. Let us place this value in the left side of (69.7) applied to the giant, where P_e is now the only unknown. We find $P_e = 0.69$ barye.

Let us next calculate the ionization of strontium in the atmospheres of the two stars. $I = 5.67$ eV, log $(2u^+/u) = 0.32$. For the dwarf ($T_e = 5520°$ K, log $P_e = 1.30$) we obtain $N^+/N \simeq 525$; for the giant ($T_e = 4650°$ K, log $P_e = -0.16$) $N^+/N \simeq 1052$. The proportion of Sr^+ ions is about doubled in the giant, from which follows the stronger intensity of the 4077–4215 lines, used as the luminosity criterion.

73. Equilibrium between atoms and molecules

Guldberg and Waage's law of mass action, applied to the equilibrium reaction between two atoms A and B and to the molecule AB

$$A + B \rightleftharpoons AB$$

leads to an equation completely similar to that of Saha. If P_A, P_B and P_{AB} are the partial pressures of the three constituents, we obtain

$$\frac{P_A P_B}{P_{AB}} = \frac{u_A u_B}{u_{AB}} \frac{(2\pi M)^{3/2}}{h^3} (kT)^{5/2} e^{-(D/kT)},$$

where D is the dissociation energy of the molecule AB, M is the reduced mass $M = M_A M_B/(M_A + M_B)$ and u_{AB} the partition function of the molecule. The expression for this latter quantity involves the electronic energy u_e, the rotational energy u_r and the vibrational energy u_v

$$u_{AB} = \Sigma\, u_e u_r u_v,$$

the summation being carried out over the different energy levels. As a first approximation we can write:

$$u_e \simeq g_{AB},$$

statistical weight of the fundamental level of AB;

$$u_r \simeq kT8\pi^2 \mathscr{J}/h^2,$$

where $\mathscr{J}$ is the moment of inertia of the molecule;

$$u_v = (1 - e^{-(h\nu/kT)})^{-1},$$

where ν is the frequency of the fundamental vibration.

Russell (1934) has studied in this way the equilibrium relative to the principal diatomic molecules in the stellar atmospheres, for the dwarfs, and for the giants where the pressure is less. In these latter stars the CN molecules ought to be more abundant and the lines stronger (§ 36). They should exhibit their maximum intensity in K1 giants ($T \simeq 4000°$ K) and in K4 dwarfs ($T \simeq 4380°$ K). One predicts a much less pronounced intensity difference between giants and dwarfs in the case of CH bands (§ 36).

The intensity of the TiO bands must reach its maximum in dwarfs of type M5, while it continues to increase in giants of lower temperatures. Sure enough, the classification of dwarf stars, based on the intensity of the TiO bands (§ 39), does not show dwarfs of types more advanced than M5.

74. Applications of curves of growth

The measurements of the equivalent widths of lines (§ 45) leads, by means of the *curve of growth*, to a quantitative evaluation of the excitation temperature and electron pressure.

The theory of the formation of spectral lines [1, 16] allows us to predict how the contour of a line is modified when the number of absorbing atoms N varies (Fig. 48). When N increases, the line at

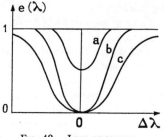

FIG. 48.   LINE PROFILES.

first progressively deepens without much widening (profiles *a* and *b*), but soon the central residual intensity stops changing (*b*). The *core* of the line is then saturated and a further increase in N has only the effect of enlarging the *wings* (profile *c*).

By integrating a series of profiles we can evaluate the equivalent width W for various values of N and construct the theoretical *curve of growth* for the line by placing on the abscissa log N, on the ordinate log W (Fig. 49). In the straight part AB (corresponding to profiles

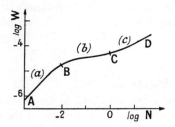

FIG. 49.   SCHEMATIC CURVE OF GROWTH.

analogous to *a* on Fig. 48) the slope is equal to unity and W is proportional to N; this is the case for weak lines. The level stretch BC (profile *b*) corresponds to the saturation. Finally, in the case of very strong lines, there follows a further straight region CD of slope 1/2 (profile *c*) where W is proportional to N.

Experimentally we can obtain some points on the curve of growth in the spectrum of a star by measuring the equivalent width of lines in the same multiplet, assuming the same lower level of excitation, if we know the relative probabilities of the various transitions. The intensity of the line is in fact proportional to the product of the number of absorbing atoms N_i and the *oscillator strength f* corresponding to the transition considered. In certain cases this latter quantity can be calculated by the theory of multiplets or deduced from laboratory measurements of the intensity.[6]

We construct the curve of growth for a multiplet by placing on the abscissa $\log (Nf)$ and on the ordinate, as suggested by theory, $\log (W/\lambda)$. It is defined with a sliding along the axis of the abscissa, since N_i is an unknown constant. By proceeding similarly for two multiplets of the same atom having different lower levels i and i', we can bring the two curves into coincidence by a translation parallel to the abscissa. This latter determines the ratio N_i/N_i' if this time we know the *absolute* values of the oscillator strengths. The method can be extended to any number of multiplets whatsoever and ultimately gives the distribution of atoms in the different excitation levels. From the Boltzmann formula we then derive the excitation temperature.

Let us suppose that we have finally constructed in an analogous manner the curves of growth for a neutral atom and the same atom in an ionized state. If the excitation temperatures which have been deduced are nearly identical, the translation that must be made to the curve of growth of the neutral atom in order to bring it into coincidence with that of the ionized atom yields the ratio N^+/N, that is, the left-hand side of the Saha formula. By taking as the ionization temperature the excitation temperature found previously, the only unknown remaining in the right-hand side is the electron pressure, which we can therefore calculate. Finally, we derive the gas pressure P_g if we know the relative abundance of the elements.

75. Relative abundances

One of the most often used methods for evaluating relative abundances depends once more on the use of the curve of growth. The superposition of curves relative to two different atoms, A and B,

---

[6] The oscillator strength is proportional to the Einstein transition probability B_{ij}:

$$f_{ij} = m_e h \nu B_{ij}/\pi\epsilon^2.$$

m_e and ϵ are the mass and charge of the electron, ν the frequency of the line. The name arises from the fact that, in the old vibrational theory, f_{ij} represented the number of elementary oscillators equivalent to the atom.

leads effectively to the determination of the ratio N_A/N_B in the manner in which we have evaluated the ratio N^+/N for a given element. For a rather low temperature it is also necessary to take into account the atoms held in molecular combinations (§ 73). The calculations are always complex and *model atmospheres* (§ 76) most often play a role.

In the solar atmosphere the abundances of about 60 different elements have been determined. About 30 stars of classes O to G have also been studied since the classic work of Unsöld on τ Sco, type B0 (1941). Table IX gives the results of several recent determinations relating to stars of types O9 to A0, plus an extract of values found for the most abundant atoms in the solar atmosphere. $\mathfrak{N}$ represents the total number of atoms of the same kind in all states of ionization and combination, and in each case $\mathfrak{N}$ has been taken arbitrarily as 1000 for hydrogen.

As a whole, the differences of chemical composition seem of the order of the probable errors, which can exceed 50% or even 100% in the case of elements with low abundances. It is particularly difficult to evaluate the abundance of helium. Recent work (Miss Underhill, de Jager and Neven) gives for the ratio N_{He}/N_H 6% instead of 17%, and one cannot yet say which of the two values should be preferred. It is therefore impossible at present to conclude with certainty that a real difference in chemical composition exists between atmospheres of normal stars, giants or dwarfs of classes O to G belonging to population I.

The peculiarities in the "metallic line stars" associated with class A could result from a special structure of their atmosphere, where the convective zone may be near the surface. But we do know some O and B stars certainly deficient in hydrogen, where the helium lines are intense and the Balmer lines weak or absent.

Besides these exceptional cases, the differences of chemical composition most probably concern the Wolf-Rayet stars and the red stars of classes M, S and C, for which, however, we do not yet have quantitative evaluations.

It appears difficult to interpret the existence of the two parallel *WC* and *WN* series (§ 40) other than by an important difference in the relative abundances of carbon–oxygen and nitrogen. For the red stars, P. W. Merrill (1955) constructed a diagram relating the spectral type to two parameters: the relative abundance of carbon and oxygen on the one hand, that of titanium and zirconium on the other (representatives respectively of the light and heavy metals). When the oxygen is less abundant than the carbon, it combines with it entirely to form CO molecules, which do not reveal themselves in the observable

TABLE IX

RELATIVE ABUNDANCES OF THE ELEMENTS

Elements	Sun G2 V (Goldberg, Müller, Aller) 1958	10 Lac O9 V (Traving) 1957	τ Sco B0 (Traving) 1955	ζ Per B1 Ia (Cayrel) 1957	α Lyr A0 V (Hunger) 1955
H	1000	1000	1000	1000	1000
He	—	170	170	204	69
C	0.36	0.23	0.23	0.18	—
N	0.10	0.23	0.36	0.20	—
O	1.00	0.59	1.29	1.08	0.74
Ne	—	0.53	0.53	0.41	—
Na	0.002	—	—	—	—
Mg	0.019	0.165	0.054	0.059	0.050
Al	0.0016	0.012	0.0038	0.0060	0.0005
Si	0.040	0.056	0.088	0.093	0.017
S	0.015	—	—	0.030	—
Ca	0.0024	—	—	—	0.0016
Fe	0.0057	—	—	—	—

spectral domain (the band most easy to examine is found at 2.4 μ). The carbon excess appears in the form of C_2 and CN molecules, and we deal with a C star. In contrast, when oxygen is more abundant than carbon, the latter is entirely used to form CO molecules and the oxygen excess forms metallic oxides. Depending on the relative abundance of Ti and of Zr we have an M or an S star.

The known spectral peculiarities of stars characteristic of population II, such as subdwarfs, are: the relative weakness of lines of hydrogen and metals in hot stars, the great intensity of CH bands in later type stars, and finally the weakness of the CN bands in the G and K giants. They could correspond to a real deficiency of hydrogen and especially of metals, or to a different structure of their atmosphere.

76. Stratified models [16]

The measurement of equivalent widths of absorption lines yields information about the average physical conditions in the absorbing layers and about their chemical compositions. But, on account of the relative transparency of the surface layers, the radiation that leaves the star arises from various depths.

Rather than using the geometric depth x computed from the surface, each elementary spherical layer is better characterized by its *optical depth* τ, defined in the same manner as optical density (§ 4), by substituting for the decimal absorption coefficient a the Naperian coefficient k

$$\tau = \int_0^x k \cdot \mathrm{d}x \quad \text{or} \quad \tau = \int_0^x \kappa \cdot \rho \cdot \mathrm{d}x, \qquad (76.1)$$

where κ represents the absorption coefficient per unit mass and ρ the density. The optical depth naturally depends on the wavelength. A given optical depth may correspond to quite different geometrical depths, according to the values of κ and ρ. The atmosphere of a dwarf star is geometrically very thin (of the order of $1/100$ of the radius in the case of the sun); that of a giant, much more rarefied, is much more extended.

The existence of a temperature gradient within the atmosphere accounts for the darkening toward the limb of the solar disk. The continuous spectrum received when we view the center of the disk (Fig. 1, § 3) has traversed the surface layers normally and originates in the mean from deeper and hotter layers than the spectrum coming from a point near the limb. This is why it is more intense and more "blue." Barbier has shown that it is possible to obtain from the observational data the temperature and pressure as a function of the optical depth, thus making possible the construction of a true *empirical model* of the solar atmosphere.

Theoretical models.—This analytic method stands in contrast to the synthetic method often used for constructing theoretical model atmospheres. One takes three parameters *a priori*: the effective temperature, the surface gravity g, and the chemical composition. This last allows the preparation of a table of absorption coefficients per unit mass as a function of wavelength. For a star of radius R and mass $\mathfrak{M}$ the surface gravity is

$$g = G\mathfrak{M}/R^2,$$

where G is the constant of universal gravitation. The radius, varying within much wider limits than the mass, is especially significant; the surface gravity is thus much greater for dwarfs than for giants.

The construction of the majority of theoretical models depends on the following hypotheses: the atmosphere, stratified in plane layers, is in radiative equilibrium and in hydrostatic equilibrium. It also satisfies the conditions of local thermodynamic equilibrium (§ 68).

Gray case.—The calculations are greatly simplified by using a conveniently chosen mean absorption coefficient $\bar{\kappa}$, independent of wavelength.

This is the *gray case* that often leads to a valid first approximation. To the variation in geometric depth dx corresponds, according to (76.1), the variation in optical depth

$$d\tau = \kappa \cdot \rho \cdot dx. \tag{76.2}$$

The hypotheses of radiative equilibrium and local thermodynamic equilibrium give a relation between the temperature T, the optical depth τ and the effective temperature T_e.

$$T^4 = \tfrac{1}{2} T_e^4 (1 + \tfrac{3}{2}\tau). \tag{76.3}$$

The temperature at the optical depth $\tau = \tfrac{2}{3}$ is thus equal to the effective temperature, and the surface temperature $(\tau = 0)$ is $T_0 = T_e/\sqrt[4]{2} = 0.811 \cdot T_e$. The fact that it is often lower shows that the approximation obtained in the gray case can be insufficient.

Let P_r be the radiation pressure. Hydrostatic equilibrium gives the variation of total pressure as a function of geometric depth

$$d(P_g + P_r) = \rho \cdot g \cdot dx,$$

but the radiation pressure plays a role only in the very hot stars. In all the other cases one can simply write

$$dP_g = \rho \cdot g \cdot dx. \tag{76.4}$$

By eliminating ρ and x between (76.2) and (76.4), we obtain

$$\frac{dP_g}{d\tau} = \frac{g}{\kappa} \quad \text{or} \quad \frac{dP_g}{dT}\frac{dT}{d\tau} = \frac{g}{\kappa}.$$

Integration of this differential equation between P_g and T, with the condition $P_g = 0$ for $\tau = 0$, gives the variation of pressure as a function of the temperature and, by the use of (76.3), as a function of τ. The perfect gas law also gives ρ as a function of T, and therefore of τ. Then, equation (76.2) allows τ to be expressed as a function of x. We thus finally have for each depth x the optical depth, density, pressure and temperature.

Non-gray case.—The introduction of an absorption coefficient varying with wavelength permits a closer approach to reality. In the hot stars the hydrogen atom is mainly responsible for the absorption. Along the continuous spectra that extend the Lyman, Balmer and Paschen series (§ 29), the absorption diminishes toward shorter wavelengths almost proportionally to λ^3. But it is also necessary to consider the continuous absorption that results from the passage of an electron in the vicinity of a proton ("free-free" transition).

In stars of lower temperature, such as the sun, the principal absorption in the visible and near infrared is caused by the negative hydrogen ion, H^-, formed by the combination of an electron with a neutral atom (Wildt, 1938). It is maximal around 0.83μ. It is necessary to include the absorption resulting from the passage of an electron in the vicinity of a neutral H atom ("free-free"), which increases monotonically toward the infrared. The superposition of the two curves gives an absorption minimum around 1.65μ.

Finally, the models calculated in the gray or non-gray cases allow the determination of the energy distribution in the continuous spectrum, of the size of the Balmer discontinuity, etc. After we construct a certain number of models, with different values of the initial parameters, it is possible to see which of these is the best fit to the star under study by matching the results of the calculations and the observations.

77. Empirical classification parameters and theoretical parameters

The empirical classification parameters are connected in a more or less direct manner to the three parameters used in the construction of models: effective temperature, surface gravity and chemical composition. In the Yerkes classification (§ 39) the spectral type roughly corresponds to the temperature, the luminosity class to the electron pressure, itself related to the surface gravity (§ 76). In the two-parameter classification of Barbier and Chalonge (§ 52) the size D and position λ_1 of the Balmer discontinuity are functions of temperature and pressure. The pressure acts especially on λ_1 by the interatomic Stark effect (§ 29).

The blue gradient appears to depend essentially on the temperature when we consider only population I stars. But the points plotted for stars of population II, whose *total* chemical composition is probably different (§ 78), clearly fall outside the surface Σ. For the same values of D and of λ_1, Φ_b is smaller than in population I. Thus the gradient can also depend on chemical composition. But rather than change the chemical composition of the atmosphere, involving a modification to the absorption coefficients, we can assume that it is a question of a change of structure in connection with the total chemical composition.

78. A sketch of ideas on the probable evolution of stars
[17, 24, 29]

The theory of stellar interiors shows that the configuration of a *homogeneous* gaseous mass, free of rotation or rotating slowly, is entirely determined by its chemical composition and mass.   These two parameters suffice to fix the position of the point plotted on the H-R diagram.   With the chemical composition of the sun and of various masses, we can calculate a series of homogeneous models, which on the diagram align themselves rather well along the main sequence (with the most massive toward the top).   This should therefore represent stars of the same chemical composition but of different masses.

Evolution can result either from a change of chemical composition or a variation of mass.   The first cause is without doubt the more important.   In fact, the thermonuclear reactions, whatever may be the mechanism in action, have the effect of slowly converting the hydrogen contained in the central convective region into helium, with a release of energy.   But the chemical composition cannot be modified at the same time in the outer regions, which remain in radiative equilibrium.   Thus the small difference found in the composition of atmospheres between the giants and dwarfs of the two populations is explained.   At the center of the star there develops a nucleus deprived of hydrogen, which becomes isothermal.   The energy production is then confined to a thin envelope around this nucleus.   The results of calculations by Schönberg and Chandrasekhar (1942) show that the star remains in the vicinity of the main sequence until a certain critical fraction q_c of its hydrogen mass is transformed into helium. When this limit is reached, a change in structure occurs, such that the radius of the star increases and its effective temperature diminishes. On the color-luminosity diagram the plotted point is displaced toward the right, in the direction of the yellow giants.   *The evolution is accordingly more rapid as the star is more massive, and thus more luminous.*

The evolutionary trajectives calculated by Kushwaha (1957) for the masses $\mathfrak{M} = 10.5$ and 2.5 ⊙ are represented by dots in Figure 50. The broken curve shows what has happened to the original main sequence (the solid line) after 33.9 million years.   Hoyle and Schwarzschild (1955) have treated the case of stars with masses 1.1 and 1.2 ⊙: the models calculated with increasing values of q ($> q_c$) lead to a diagram rather analogous to those of the globular clusters (Fig. 22, § 38): a quasi-vertical ascent up to the red giant branch, traversed at first from left to right toward the high luminosities and lower temperatures, then in the reverse direction from right to left (the "horizontal branch").

The results allow the individualities of the cluster diagrams where all the stars must be born almost simultaneously with the same chemical composition, to be attributed to age differences.   At their

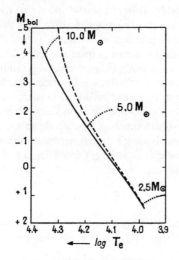

FIG. 50.   EVOLUTION BEGINNING FROM THE MAIN SEQUENCE (KUSHWAHA).

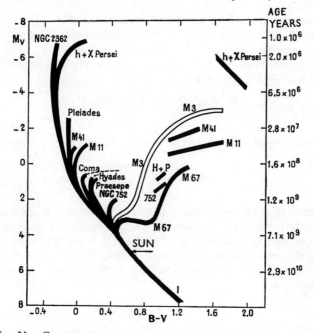

FIG. 51.   COLOR-LUMINOSITY DIAGRAMS OF VARIOUS GALACTIC CLUSTERS
AND A GLOBULAR CLUSTER (M3), ACCORDING TO SANDAGE (1958).

origin they probably differed only in their masses. The most luminous, which are also the most massive, are the first to leave the main sequence. The position of the upper end of the main sequence, marked by a turn, thus informs us qualitatively of the age of the cluster (Fig. 51). Ambartzumian's O associations, which contain very hot stars, are very recent formations. Clusters containing B stars are younger than those whose most brilliant components belong to class A. The very old clusters no longer contain stars earlier than F.

Quantitatively an attempt may be made to evaluate the age of a cluster from the equivalence between mass and energy (Einstein's relation). The energy E (in ergs) freed by the destruction of mass $\Delta\mathfrak{M}$ (grams) has the expression

$$E = c^2 \cdot \Delta\mathfrak{M}, \tag{78.1}$$

where c is the velocity of light in cm/sec. The conversion to helium from a mass of hydrogen $\mathfrak{M}_H$ causes the disappearance of mass

$$\Delta\mathfrak{M} = 0.007\mathfrak{M}_H. \tag{78.2}$$

If the total mass of the star is $\mathfrak{M}_0$ (g) and the initial hydrogen mass is $X\mathfrak{M}_0$ ($X < 1$), the mass of hydrogen transformed into helium at the time t when the star leaves the main sequence is $\mathfrak{M}_H = q_c \cdot X \cdot \mathfrak{M}_0$ and the energy E_t liberated by this time since the origin is, according to (78.1) and (78.2),

$$E_t = 0.007c^2 \cdot q_c \cdot X \cdot \mathfrak{M}_0 \text{ (ergs)}.$$

If we assume the power W_t radiated by the star (erg/s) to be constant, we can write that the elapsed duration since its origin is

$$t = \frac{E_t}{W_t} = 0.007c^2 \cdot q_c \cdot X \cdot \frac{\mathfrak{M}_0}{W_t} \text{ (seconds)}. \tag{78.3}$$

According to the evolutionary models of Schönberg and Chandrasekhar the product $q_c X$ is practically independent of the mass $\mathfrak{M}_0$ and equals 0.07. By expressing the duration t in years ($3.156 \cdot 10^7$ s), by taking the solar mass as the unit of mass ($1.991 \cdot 10^{33}$ g), and as unit of power the power radiated by the sun ($4.48 \cdot 10^{33}$ erg/s) the formula becomes

$$t = 0.62 \cdot 10^{10} \frac{\mathfrak{M}_0}{W_t} \text{ years}.$$

Actually W begins to increase before the limit q_c is reached. By taking the value W_t on the average too great, we will underestimate t. Instead of (78.3) we must write

$$t = 0.007c^2\mathfrak{M}_0 X \int_0^{q_c} \frac{\mathrm{d}q}{W(q)},$$

by considering W as a function of q, which can be evaluated from the theory. Sandage (1958) [24] thus arrived at the expression

$$t = 1.10 \cdot 10^{10} \frac{\mathfrak{M}_0}{W_t} \text{ years.} \qquad (78.4)$$

The absolute magnitude M_v and the bolometric correction give W_t, and we derive $\mathfrak{M}$ from the mass-luminosity relation (§ 67).

It is by means of relation (78.4) that the vertical axis of Figure 51 has been calibrated in years. (The calibration is valid only for the upper portion of the main sequence.) The h-χ Persei cluster should be about 1 million years old, the Pleiades about 20 million, the Hyades and Praesepe about 400 million years. Finally, the age of the cluster M67, whose diagram resembles that of a globular cluster, would be in the order of 5000 million years.

For the globular clusters such as M3 we find ages in the order of 5000 to 7000 million years.

The evolutionary scheme outlined above has the mass practically constant, because the diminution of mass accompanying the conversion of hydrogen to helium is, from this point of view, negligible. But it is possible that the hot stars lose part of their mass by emitting corpuscular radiation, which is, moreover, very poorly understood. This hypothesis, which complicates the phenomena and leads clearly to a certain evolution along the main sequence, has been developed by the Russian astronomers (Fessenkov, Massevich, etc.)

From the precise knowledge of color-luminosity diagrams of clusters, we have acquired over the last several years the essential data on the probable evolution of stars beginning from the main sequence. We have been led to conclude that the populations I and II differ essentially in their age. We have also begun to think that all the intermediate types exist between them, and that an old population I resembles a relatively recent population II.

We hold less satisfactory information on the first and especially the last stages of evolution. The stars certainly form—and often in groups—by condensation from the interstellar matter, and, by gravitational contraction, they must join the main sequence rapidly at a point that depends on their mass. The O associations and the T associations (formed of red dwarfs) contain only young stars that have been born from the usually apparent masses of interstellar gas accompanying them. On the other hand, there are generally no young stars in globular clusters, in elliptical galaxies and the nuclei of spirals, since the initial matter is completely used up there.

We are inclined to think that the unstable stars, the novae and the nuclei of planetary nebulae correspond to the end of the life of a star, whose final stage is represented by white dwarfs.

TABLE X

PHYSICAL AND ASTRONOMICAL CONSTANTS

Velocity of light *in vacuo* .... $c = 2.9978 \cdot 10^{10}$ cm·s^{-1}

Charge of the electron .... $\epsilon = 4.802 \cdot 10^{-10}$ E.S.U.

Mass of the electron .... $m_e = 9.106 \cdot 10^{-28}$ g

Mass of the hydrogen atom .... $m_H = 1.6734 \cdot 10^{-24}$ g

1 electron volt .... 1 eV $= 1.602 \cdot 10^{-12}$ erg

Boltzmann's constant .... $k = 1.3803 \cdot 10^{-16}$ erg·degree^{-1}

Planck's constant .... $h = 6.6234 \cdot 10^{-27}$ erg·s

Constants in Planck's law
(spectral radiance) .... $\begin{cases} C_1 = 2\pi hc^2 = 3.740 \cdot 10^{-5} \text{ erg} \cdot \text{cm}^2 \cdot \text{s}^{-1} \\ C_2 = hc/k = 1.4385 \text{ cm} \cdot \text{degree} \end{cases}$

Stefan's constant .... $\sigma = 2\pi^5 k^4 / 15 c^2 h^3 = 5.6724 \cdot 10^{-5}$ erg·cm^{-2}·s^{-1}·degree^{-4}

Gravitational constant .... $G = 6.670 \cdot 10^{-8}$ dynes·cm^2·g^{-2}

1 astronomical unit .... 1 A.U. $= 1.496 \cdot 10^{13}$ cm

1 parsec .... 1 pc $= 206265$ A.U. $= 3.086 \cdot 10^{18}$ cm

Constants relating to the sun

Radius, mass, density .... $R = 6.975 \cdot 10^{10}$ cm, $\mathfrak{M} = 1.991 \cdot 10^{33}$ g, $d = 1.41$ g·cm^{-3}

Solar constant .... $E = 1.595 \cdot 10^6$ erg·cm^{-2}·s^{-1} $= 2.0$ cal·g·cm^{-2}·min^{-1}

Effective temperature .... $T_e = 5800°$ K

Apparent photovisual magnitude .... $m_{pv} = -26.73$

,, photographic ,, ... $m_{pg} = -26.20$

,, bolometric ,, ... $m_b = -26.79$

Absolute photovisual magnitude .... $M_{pv} = 4.84$

,, photographic ,, ... $M_{pg} = 5.27$

,, bolometric ,, ... $M_b = 4.78$

TABLE XI

ABBREVIATIONS OF THE NAMES OF CONSTELLATIONS CITED

And	Andromeda (ae)	Cyg	Cygnus (i)	Peg	Pegasus (i)
Aql	Aquila (ae)	Dra	Draco (onis)	Per	Perseus (i)
Aqr	Aquarius (ii)	Eri	Eridanus (i)	Psc	Pisces (ium)
Ari	Aries (etis)	Gem	Gemini (orum)	Pup	Puppis (is)
Aur	Auriga (ae)	Her	Hercules (is)	Sge	Sagitta (ae)
Boo	Bootes (is)	Hyd	Hydra (ae)	Sco	Scorpius (ii)
Cas	Cassiopeia (eiae)	Leo	Leo (onis)	Tau	Taurus (i)
Cen	Centaurus (i)	Lep	Lepus (oris)	Tri	Triangulum (i)
Cep	Cepheus (ei)	Lyr	Lyra (ae)	UMa	Ursa Major (ae-oris)
Cet	Cetus (i)	Mon	Monoceros (otis)	UMi	Ursa Minor (ae-oris)
CMa	Canis Major (oris)	Oph	Ophiuchus (i)	Vir	Virgo (inis)
CMi	Canis Minor (oris)	Ori	Orion (onis)		

Note: the Latin genitive endings, used for designating specific stars, are given in parentheses. *Example: α Ursae Majoris.*

BRIEF BIBLIOGRAPHY

1. ALLER, L. A., *Astrophysics. The Atmospheres of the Sun and Stars*, New York, Ronald Press, 2nd ed., 1963.
2. BARBIER, D., *Les atmosphères stellaires*, Paris, Flammarion, 1952.
3. BEER, A., ed., *Vistas in Astronomy*, 2 vol., London, Pergamon Press, 1956.
4. BRUHAT, G., *Les étoiles*, Paris, Alcan, 1939.
5. ———, *Optique*, 4th edition, revised and completed by A. Kastler, Paris, Masson, 1954.
6. CABANNES, J., *Optique ondulatoire*, Paris, Sedes, 1954.
7. *Centennial Symposia*, Harvard Observatory, Cambridge (Mass.), 1948.
8. DANJON, A., *Astronomie générale*, Paris, Sennac, 1953.
9. ——— and COUDER, A., *Lunettes et télescopes*, Paris, Édit. Revue d'Optique, 1935.
10. ———, PRUVOST, P. and BLACHE, J., *Le Ciel et la Terre*, Encyclopédie française, vol. III, Paris, 1956.
11. DELHAYE, J., *Astronomie stellaire*, Paris, Collection A. Colin, No. 284, 1953.
12. DUFAY, J., *Galactic Nebulae and Interstellar Matter* (translated by A. J. Pomerans), New York, Philosophical Library, 1957.
13. EBERHARD, E., KOHLSCHÜTTER, A. and LUDENDORFF, H., ed., *Handbuch der Astrophysik*, 10 vol., Berlin, Springer, 1928–1936.
14. FABRY, Ch., *Introduction générale à la photométrie*, Paris, Édit. Revue d'Optique, 1927.
15. ———, *Les radiations*, Paris, Collection A. Colin, No. 243, 1946.
16. FLÜGGE, S., ed., *Encyclopedia of Physics*, vol. L, Astrophysics I, Berlin, Springer, 1958.
17. *Ibid.*, vol. LI, Astrophysics II, Berlin, Springer, 1959.
18. GREENSTEIN, J. L., ed., *The Hertzsprung-Russell Diagram*, Moscow I.A.U. Symposium, Paris, Annales d'Astrophysique, Supplement No. 10, 1959.
19. GOLDBERG, L. and ALLER, L. A., *Atoms, Stars and Nebulae*, Philadelphia, Blakiston, 1943.
20. HYNEK, J. A., ed., *Astrophysics: A topical symposium*, New York, Toronto, London, McGraw-Hill, 1951.

21. IRWIN, J. B., ed., *Astronomical Photoelectric Conference, Lowell Observatory*, 1953. Proceedings National Science Foundation, Indiana University.

22. LALLEMAND, A. and MUNSCH, M., "Les cellules photoélectriques," in: SURUGUE, J., ed., *Techniques générales du laboratoire de physique*, vol. 1, Paris, C.N.R.S., 1947. See also "Photomultipliers," in HILTNER, W. A., ed., *Astronomical Techniques*, University of Chicago Press, 1962.

23. MICHEL, P., *La spectroscopie d'émission*, Paris, Collection A. Colin, No. 280, 1953.

24. O'CONNELL, D. J. K., ed., *Stellar Populations*, Proceedings of the Conference sponsored by the Pontifical Academy of Science and the Vatican Observatory. Amsterdam, North-Holland Publishing Co.; New York, Interscience Publishers, 1958.

25. PECKER, J. C. and SCHATZMAN, E., *Astrophysique générale*, Paris, Masson, 1959.

26. PICART, L., *Astronomie générale*, Paris, Collection A. Colin, No. 50, 1924.

27. *Principes fondamentaux de classification stellaire*, Paris, Colloques internationaux du C.N.R.S., 1953.

28. *Problèmes de populations stellaires et de structure de la Galaxie*, Paris, Colloques nationaux du C.N.R.S., 1957.

29. SCHWARZSCHILD, M., *Structure and Evolution of the Stars*, Princeton University Press, 1958.

30. STRUVE, O., *Stellar Evolution*, Princeton University Press, 1950.

31. UNSÖLD, A., *Physik der Sternatmosphären*, 2nd edition, Berlin, Springer, 1955.

32. WOOD, F. B., ed., *Astronomical Photoelectric Photometry*, Philadelphia symposium, New York, American Association for the Advancement of Science, 1953.

33. ZWORYKIN, V. K. and RAMBERG, E. G., *La photoélectricité et ses applications* (traduit par H. Aberdam), Paris, Dunod, 1953.

INDEX

CATALOG OF DOVER BOOKS

CHEMISTRY AND PHYSICAL CHEMISTRY

ORGANIC CHEMISTRY, F. C. Whitmore. The entire subject of organic chemistry for the ·practicing chemist and the advanced student. Storehouse of facts, theories, processes found elsewhere only in specialized journals. Covers aliphatic compounds (500 pages on the properties and synthetic preparation of hydrocarbons, halides, proteins, ketones, etc.), alicyclic compounds, aromatic compounds, heterocyclic compounds, organophosphorus and organometallic compounds. Methods of synthetic preparation analyzed critically throughout. Includes much of biochemical interest. "The scope of this volume is astonishing," INDUSTRIAL AND ENGINEERING CHEMISTRY. 12,000-reference index. 2387-item bibliography. Total of x + 1005pp. 5⅜ x 8. Two volume set.
S700 Vol I Paperbound **$2.00**
S701 Vol II Paperbound **$2.00**
The set **$4.00**

THE PRINCIPLES OF ELECTROCHEMISTRY, D. A. MacInnes. Basic equations for almost every subfield of electrochemistry from first principles, referring at all times to the soundest and most recent theories and results; unusually useful as text or as reference. Covers coulometers and Faraday's Law, electrolytic conductance, the Debye-Hueckel method for the theoretical calculation of activity coefficients, concentration cells, standard electrode potentials, thermodynamic ionization constants, pH, potentiometric titrations, irreversible phenomena, Planck's equation, and much more. "Excellent treatise," AMERICAN CHEMICAL SOCIETY JOURNAL. "Highly recommended," CHEMICAL AND METALLURGICAL ENGINEERING. 2 Indices. Appendix. 585-item bibliography. 137 figures. 94 tables. ii + 478pp. 5⅝ x 8⅜.
S52 Paperbound **$2.35**

THE CHEMISTRY OF URANIUM: THE ELEMENT, ITS BINARY AND RELATED COMPOUNDS, J. J. Katz and E. Rabinowitch. Vast post-World War II collection and correlation of thousands of AEC reports and published papers in a useful and easily accessible form, still the most complete and up-to-date compilation. Treats "dry uranium chemistry," occurrences, preparation, properties, simple compounds, isotopic composition, extraction from ores, spectra, alloys, etc. Much material available only here. Index. Thousands of evaluated bibliographical references. 324 tables, charts, figures. xxi + 609pp. 5⅜ x 8.
S757 Paperbound **$2.95**

KINETIC THEORY OF LIQUIDS, J. Frenkel. Regarding the kinetic theory of liquids as a generalization and extension of the theory of solid bodies, this volume covers all types of arrangements of solids, thermal displacements of atoms, interstitial atoms and ions, orientational and rotational motion of molecules, and transition between states of matter. Mathematical theory is developed close to the physical subject matter. 216 bibliographical footnotes. 55 figures. xi + 485pp. 5⅜ x 8.
S94 Clothbound **$3.95**
S95 Paperbound **$2.45**

POLAR MOLECULES, Pieter Debye. This work by Nobel laureate Debye offers a complete guide to fundamental electrostatic field relations, polarizability, molecular structure. Partial contents: electric intensity, displacement and force, polarization by orientation, molar polarization and molar refraction, halogen-hydrides, polar liquids, ionic saturation, dielectric constant, etc. Special chapter considers quantum theory. Indexed. 172pp. 5⅜ x 8.
S64 Paperbound **$1.50**

ELASTICITY, PLASTICITY AND STRUCTURE OF MATTER, R. Houwink. Standard treatise on rheological aspects of different technically important solids such as crystals, resins, textiles, rubber, clay, many others. Investigates general laws for deformations; determines divergences from these laws for certain substances. Covers general physical and mathematical aspects of plasticity, elasticity, viscosity. Detailed examination of deformations, internal structure of matter in relation to elastic and plastic behavior, formation of solid matter from a fluid, conditions for elastic and plastic behavior of matter. Treats glass, asphalt, gutta percha, balata, proteins, baker's dough, lacquers, sulphur, others. 2nd revised, enlarged edition. Extensive revised bibliography in over 500 footnotes. Index. Table of symbols. 214 figures. xviii + 368pp. 6 x 9¼.
S385 Paperbound **$2.45**

THE PHASE RULE AND ITS APPLICATION, Alexander Findlay. Covering chemical phenomena of 1, 2, 3, 4, and multiple component systems, this "standard work on the subject" (NATURE, London), has been completely revised and brought up to date by A. N. Campbell and N. O. Smith. Brand new material has been added on such matters as binary, tertiary liquid equilibria, solid solutions in ternary systems, quinary systems of salts and water. Completely revised to triangular coordinates in ternary systems, clarified graphic representation, solid models, etc. 9th revised edition. Author, subject indexes. 236 figures. 505 footnotes, mostly bibliographic. xii + 494pp. 5⅜ x 8.
S91 Paperbound **$2.45**

TERNARY SYSTEMS: INTRODUCTION TO THE THEORY OF THREE COMPONENT SYSTEMS, G. Masing. Furnishes detailed discussion of representative types of 3-components systems, both in solid models (particularly metallic alloys) and isothermal models. Discusses mechanical mixture without compounds and without solid solutions; unbroken solid solution series; solid solutions with solubility breaks in two binary systems; iron-silicon-aluminum alloys; allotropic forms of iron in ternary system; other topics. Bibliography. Index. 166 illustrations. 178pp. 5⅝ x 8⅜. S631 Paperbound **$1.45**

THE STORY OF ALCHEMY AND EARLY CHEMISTRY, J. M. Stillman. An authoritative, scholarly work, highly readable, of development of chemical knowledge from 4000 B.C. to downfall of phlogiston theory in late 18th century. Every important figure, many quotations. Brings alive curious, almost incredible history of alchemical beliefs, practices, writings of Arabian Prince Oneeyade, Vincent of Beauvais, Geber, Zosimos, Paracelsus, Vitruvius, scores more. Studies work, thought of Black, Cavendish, Priestley, Van Helmont, Bergman, Lavoisier, Newton, etc. Index. Bibliography. 579pp. 5⅜ x 8. S628 Paperbound **$2.45**

See also: **ATOMIC SPECTRA AND ATOMIC STRUCTURE, G. Herzberg; INVESTIGATIONS ON THE THEORY OF THE BROWNIAN MOVEMENT, A. Einstein; TREATISE ON THERMODYNAMICS, M. Planck.**

ASTRONOMY AND ASTROPHYSICS

AN ELEMENTARY SURVEY OF CELESTIAL MECHANICS, Y. Ryabov. Elementary exposition of gravitational theory and celestial mechanics. Historical introduction and coverage of basic principles, including: the elliptic, the orbital plane, the 2- and 3-body problems, the discovery of Neptune, planetary rotation, the length of the day, the shapes of galaxies, satellites (detailed treatment of Sputnik I), etc. First American reprinting of successful Russian popular exposition. Elementary algebra and trigonometry helpful, but not necessary; presentation chiefly verbal. Appendix of theorem proofs. 58 figures. 165pp. 5⅜ x 8.
T756 Paperbound **$1.25**

THE SKY AND ITS MYSTERIES, E. A. Beet. One of most lucid books on mysteries of universe; deals with astronomy from earliest observations to latest theories of expansion of universe, source of stellar energy, birth of planets, origin of moon craters, possibility of life on other planets. Discusses effects of sunspots on weather; distances, ages of several stars; master plan of universe; methods and tools of astronomers; much more. "Eminently readable book," London Times. Extensive bibliography. Over 50 diagrams. 12 full-page plates, fold-out star map. Introduction. Index, 238pp. 5¼ x 7½. T627 Clothbound **$3.00**

THE REALM OF THE NEBULAE, E. Hubble. One of the great astronomers of our time records his formulation of the concept of "island universes," and its impact on astronomy. Such topics are covered as the velocity-distance relation; classification, nature, distances, general field of nebulae; cosmological theories; nebulae in the neighborhood of the Milky Way. 39 photos of nebulae, nebulae clusters, spectra of nebulae, and velocity distance relations shown by spectrum comparison. "One of the most progressive lines of astronomical research," The Times (London). New introduction by A. Sandage. 55 illustrations. Index. iv + 201pp. 5⅜ x 8. S455 Paperbound **$1.50**

OUT OF THE SKY, H. H. Nininger. A non-technical but comprehensive introduction to "meteoritics", the young science concerned with all aspects of the arrival of matter from outer space. Written by one of the world's experts on meteorites, this work shows how, despite difficulties of observation and sparseness of data, a considerable body of knowledge has arisen. It defines meteors and meteorites; studies fireball clusters and processions, meteorite composition, size, distribution, showers, explosions, origins, craters, and much more. A true connecting link between astronomy and geology. More than 175 photos, 22 other illustrations. References. Bibliography of author's publications on meteorites. Index. viii + 336pp. 5⅜ x 8. T519 Paperbound **$1.85**

SATELLITES AND SCIENTIFIC RESEARCH, D. King-Hele. Non-technical account of the manmade satellites and the discoveries they have yielded up to the spring of 1959. Brings together information hitherto published only in hard-to-get scientific journals. Includes the life history of a typical satellite, methods of tracking, new information on the shape of the earth, zones of radiation, etc. Over 60 diagrams and 6 photographs. Mathematical appendix. Bibliography of over 100 items. Index. xii + 180pp. 5⅜ x 8½. T703 Clothbound **$4.00**

HOW TO MAKE A TELESCOPE, Jean Texereau. Enables the most inexperienced to choose, design, and build an f/6 or f/8 Newtonian type reflecting telescope, with an altazimuth Couder mounting, suitable for lunar, planetary, and stellar observation. A practical step-by-step course covering every operation and every piece of equipment. Basic principles of geometric and physical optics are discussed (though unnecessary to construction), and the merits of reflectors and refractors compared. A thorough discussion of eyepieces, finders, grinding, installation, testing, using the instrument, etc. 241 figures and 38 photos show almost every operation and tool. Potential errors are anticipated as much as possible. Foreword by A. Couder. Bibliography and sources of supply listing. Index. xiii + 191pp. 6¼ x 10. T464 Clothbound **$3.50**

AN INTRODUCTORY TREATISE ON DYNAMICAL ASTRONOMY, H. C. Plummer. Unusually wide connected and concise coverage of nearly every significant branch of dynamical astronomy, stressing basic principles throughout: determination of orbits, planetary theory, lunar theory, precession and nutation, and many of their applications. Hundreds of formulas and theorems worked out completely, important methods thoroughly explained. Covers motion under a central attraction, orbits of double stars and spectroscopic binaries, the libration of the moon, and much more. Index. 8 diagrams. xxi + 343pp. 5⅝ x 8⅜. **S689 Paperbound $2.35**

A COMPENDIUM OF SPHERICAL ASTRONOMY, S. Newcomb. Long a standard collection of basic methods and formulas most useful to the working astronomer, and clear full text for students. Includes the most important common approximations; 40 pages on the method of least squares; general theory of spherical coordinates; parallax; aberration; astronomical refraction; theory of precession; proper motion of the stars; methods of deriving positions of stars; and much more. Index. 9 Appendices of tables, formulas, etc. 36 figures. xviii + 444pp. 5⅜ x 8. **S690 Paperbound $2.25**

AN INTRODUCTORY TREATISE ON THE LUNAR THEORY, E. W. Brown. Indispensable for all scientists and engineers interested in orbital calculation, satellites, or navigation of space. Only work in English to explain in detail 5 major mathematical approaches to the problem of 3 bodies, those of Laplace, de Pontécoulant, Hansen, Delaunay, and Hill. Covers expressions for mutual attraction, equations of motion, forms of solution, variations of the elements in disturbed motion, the constants and their interpretations, planetary and other disturbing influences, etc. Index. Bibliography. Tables. xvi + 292pp. 5⅝ x 8⅜.

S666 Paperbound $2.00

LES METHODES NOUVELLES DE LA MECANIQUE CELESTE, H. Poincaré. Complete text (in French) of one of Poincaré's most important works. This set revolutionized celestial mechanics: first use of integral invariants, first major application of linear differential equations, study of periodic orbits, lunar motion and Jupiter's satellites, three body problem, and many other important topics. "Started a new era . . . so extremely modern that even today few have mastered his weapons," E. T. Bell. Three volumes. Total 1282pp. 6⅛ x 9¼.
Vol. 1. S401 Paperbound **$2.75**
Vol. 2. S402 Paperbound **$2.75**
Vol. 3. S403 Paperbound **$2.75**
The set **$7.50**

SPHERICAL AND PRACTICAL ASTRONOMY, W. Chauvenet. First book in English to apply mathematical techniques to astronomical problems is still standard work. Covers almost entire field, rigorously, with over 300 examples worked out. Vol. 1, spherical astronomy, applications to nautical astronomy; determination of hour angles, parallactic angle for known stars; interpolation; parallax; laws of refraction; predicting eclipses; precession, nutation of fixed stars; etc. Vol. 2, theory, use, of instruments; telescope; measurement of arcs, angles in general; electro-chronograph; sextant, reflecting circles; zenith telescope; etc. 100-page appendix of detailed proof of Gauss' method of least squares. 5th revised edition. Index. 15 plates, 20 tables. 1340pp. 5⅜ x 8.
Vol. 1 S618 Paperbound **$2.75**
Vol. 2 S619 Paperbound **$2.75**
The set **$5.50**

THE INTERNAL CONSTITUTION OF THE STARS, Sir A. S. Eddington. Influence of this has been enormous; first detailed exposition of theory of radiative equilibrium for stellar interiors, of all available evidence for existence of diffuse matter in interstellar space. Studies quantum theory, polytropic gas spheres, mass-luminosity relations, variable stars, etc. Discussions of equations paralleled with informal exposition of intimate relationship of astrophysics with great discoveries in atomic physics, radiation. Introduction. Appendix. Index. 421pp. 5⅜ x 8. **S563 Paperbound $2.25**

ASTRONOMY OF STELLAR ENERGY AND DECAY, Martin Johnson. Middle level treatment of astronomy as interpreted by modern atomic physics. Part One is non-technical, examines physical properties, source of energy, spectroscopy, fluctuating stars, various models and theories, etc. Part Two parallels these topics, providing their mathematical foundation. "Clear, concise, and readily understandable," American Library Assoc. Bibliography. 3 indexes. 29 illustrations. 216pp. 5⅜ x 8. **S537 Paperbound $1.50**

RADIATIVE TRANSFER, S. Chandrasekhar. Definitive work in field provides foundation for analysis of stellar atmospheres, planetary illumination, sky radiation; to physicists, a study of problems analogous to those in theory of diffusion of neutrons. Partial contents: equation of transfer, isotropic scattering, H-functions, diffuse reflection and transmission, Rayleigh scattering, X, Y functions, radiative equilibrium of stellar atmospheres. Extensive bibliography. 3 appendices. 35 tables. 35 figures. 407pp. 5⅝ x 8⅜. **S599 Paperbound $2.25**

AN INTRODUCTION TO THE STUDY OF STELLAR STRUCTURE, Subrahmanyan Chandrasekhar. Outstanding treatise on stellar dynamics by one of world's greatest astrophysicists. Uses classical & modern math methods to examine relationship between loss of energy, the mass, and radius of stars in a steady state. Discusses thermodynamic laws from Caratheodory's axiomatic standpoint; adiabatic, polytropic laws; work of Ritter, Emden, Kelvin, others; Stroemgren envelopes as starter for theory of gaseous stars; Gibbs statistical mechanics (quantum); degenerate stellar configuration & theory of white dwarfs, etc. "Highest level of scientific merit," BULLETIN, AMER. MATH. SOC. Bibliography. Appendixes. Index. 33 figures. 509pp. 5⅜ x 8. **S413 Paperbound $2.75**

BOOKS EXPLAINING SCIENCE AND MATHEMATICS

THE COMMON SENSE OF THE EXACT SCIENCES, W. K. Clifford. Introduction by James Newman, edited by Karl Pearson. For 70 years this has been a guide to classical scientific and mathematical thought. Explains with unusual clarity basic concepts, such as extension of meaning of symbols, characteristics of surface boundaries, properties of plane figures, vectors, Cartesian method of determining position, etc. Long preface by Bertrand Russell. Bibliography of Clifford. Corrected, 130 diagrams redrawn. 249pp. 5⅜ x 8.
T61 Paperbound **$1.60**

SCIENCE THEORY AND MAN, Erwin Schrödinger. This is a complete and unabridged reissue of SCIENCE AND THE HUMAN TEMPERAMENT plus an additional essay: "What is an Elementary Particle?" Nobel Laureate Schrödinger discusses such topics as nature of scientific method, the nature of science, chance and determinism, science and society, conceptual models for physical entities, elementary particles and wave mechanics. Presentation is popular and may be followed by most people with little or no scientific training. "Fine practical preparation for a time when laws of nature, human institutions . . . are undergoing a critical examination without parallel," Waldemar Kaempffert, N. Y. TIMES. 192pp. 5⅜ x 8.
T428 Paperbound **$1.35**

PIONEERS OF SCIENCE, O. Lodge. Eminent scientist-expositor's authoritative, yet elementary survey of great scientific theories. Concentrating on individuals—Copernicus, Brahe, Kepler, Galileo, Descartes, Newton, Laplace, Herschel, Lord Kelvin, and other scientists—the author presents their discoveries in historical order adding biographical material on each man and full, specific explanations of their achievements. The clear and complete treatment of the post-Newtonian astronomers is a feature seldom found in other books on the subject. Index. 120 illustrations. xv + 404pp. 5⅜ x 8.
T716 Paperbound **$1.50**

THE EVOLUTION OF SCIENTIFIC THOUGHT FROM NEWTON TO EINSTEIN, A. d'Abro. Einstein's special and general theories of relativity, with their historical implications, are analyzed in non-technical terms. Excellent accounts of the contributions of Newton, Riemann, Weyl, Planck, Eddington, Maxwell, Lorentz and others are treated in terms of space and time, equations of electromagnetics, finiteness of the universe, methodology of science. 21 diagrams. 482pp. 5⅜ x 8.
T2 Paperound **$2.00**

THE RISE OF THE NEW PHYSICS, A. d'Abro. A half-million word exposition, formerly titled THE DECLINE OF MECHANISM, for readers not versed in higher mathematics. The only thorough explanation, in everyday language, of the central core of modern mathematical physical theory, treating both classical and modern theoretical physics, and presenting in terms almost anyone can understand the equivalent of 5 years of study of mathematical physics. Scientifically impeccable coverage of mathematical-physical thought from the Newtonian system up through the electronic theories of Dirac and Heisenberg and Fermi's statistics. Combines both history and exposition; provides a broad yet unified and detailed view, with constant comparison of classical and modern views on phenomena and theories. "A must for anyone doing serious study in the physical sciences," JOURNAL OF THE FRANKLIN INSTITUTE. "Extraordinary faculty . . . to explain ideas and theories of theoretical physics in the language of daily life," ISIS. First part of set covers philosophy of science, drawing upon the practice of Newton, Maxwell, Poincaré, Einstein, others, discussing modes of thought, experiment, interpretations of causality, etc. In the second part, 100 pages explain grammar and vocabulary of mathematics, with discussions of functions, groups, series, Fourier series, etc. The remainder is devoted to concrete, detailed coverage of both classical and quantum physics, explaining such topics as analytic mechanics, Hamilton's principle, wave theory of light, electromagnetic waves, groups of transformations, thermodynamics, phase rule, Brownian movement, kinetics, special relativity, Planck's original quantum theory, Bohr's atom, Zeeman effect, Broglie's wave mechanics, Heisenberg's uncertainty, Eigen-values, matrices, scores of other important topics. Discoveries and theories are covered for such men as Alembert, Born, Cantor, Debye, Euler, Foucault, Galois, Gauss, Hadamard, Kelvin, Kepler, Laplace, Maxwell, Pauli, Rayleigh, Volterra, Weyl, Young, more than 180 others. Indexed. 97 illustrations. ix + 982pp. 5⅜ x 8.
T3 Volume 1, Paperbound **$2.00**
T4 Volume 2, Paperbound **$2.00**

CONCERNING THE NATURE OF THINGS, Sir William Bragg. Christmas lectures delivered at the Royal Society by Nobel laureate. Why a spinning ball travels in a curved track; how uranium is transmuted to lead, etc. Partial contents: atoms, gases, liquids, crystals, metals, etc. No scientific background needed; wonderful for intelligent child. 32pp. of photos, 57 figures. xii + 232pp. 5⅜ x 8.
T31 Paperbound **$1.35**

THE UNIVERSE OF LIGHT, Sir William Bragg. No scientific training needed to read Nobel Prize winner's expansion of his Royal Institute Christmas Lectures. Insight into nature of light, methods and philosophy of science. Explains lenses, reflection, color, resonance, polarization, x-rays, the spectrum, Newton's work with prisms, Huygens' with polarization, Crookes' with cathode ray, etc. Leads into clear statement of 2 major historical theories of light, corpuscle and wave. Dozens of experiments you can do. 199 illus., including 2 full-page color plates. 293pp. 5⅜ x 8.
S538 Paperbound **$1.85**

PHYSICS, THE PIONEER SCIENCE, L. W. Taylor. First thorough text to place all important physical phenomena in cultural-historical framework; remains best work of its kind. Exposition of physical laws, theories developed chronologically, with great historical, illustrative experiments diagrammed, described, worked out mathematically. Excellent physics text for self-study as well as class work. Vol. 1: Heat, Sound: motion, acceleration, gravitation, conservation of energy, heat engines, rotation, heat, mechanical energy, etc. 211 illus. 407pp. 5⅜ x 8. Vol. 2: Light, Electricity: images, lenses, prisms, magnetism, Ohm's law, dynamos, telegraph, quantum theory, decline of mechanical view of nature, etc. Bibliography. 13 table appendix. Index. 551 illus. 2 color plates. 508pp. 5⅜ x 8.

Vol. 1 S565 Paperbound **$2.00**
Vol. 2 S566 Paperbound **$2.00**
The set **$4.00**

FROM EUCLID TO EDDINGTON: A STUDY OF THE CONCEPTIONS OF THE EXTERNAL WORLD, Sir Edmund Whittaker. A foremost British scientist traces the development of theories of natural philosophy from the western rediscovery of Euclid to Eddington, Einstein, Dirac, etc. The inadequacy of classical physics is contrasted with present day attempts to understand the physical world through relativity, non-Euclidean geometry, space curvature, wave mechanics, etc. 5 major divisions of examination: Space; Time and Movement; the Concepts of Classical Physics; the Concepts of Quantum Mechanics; the Eddington Universe. 212pp. 5⅜ x 8. T491 Paperbound **$1.35**

THE STORY OF ATOMIC THEORY AND ATOMIC ENERGY, J. G. Feinberg. Wider range of facts on physical theory, cultural implications, than any other similar source. Completely non-technical. Begins with first atomic theory, 600 B.C., goes through A-bomb, developments to 1959. Avogadro, Rutherford, Bohr, Einstein, radioactive decay, binding energy, radiation danger, future benefits of nuclear power, dozens of other topics, told in lively, related, informal manner. Particular stress on European atomic research. "Deserves special mention . . . authoritative," Saturday Review. Formerly "The Atom Story." New chapter to 1959. Index. 34 illustrations. 251pp. 5⅜ x 8. T625 Paperbound **$1.45**

THE STRANGE STORY OF THE QUANTUM, AN ACCOUNT FOR THE GENERAL READER OF THE GROWTH OF IDEAS UNDERLYING OUR PRESENT ATOMIC KNOWLEDGE, B. Hoffmann. Presents lucidly and expertly, with barest amount of mathematics, the problems and theories which led to modern quantum physics. Dr. Hoffmann begins with the closing years of the 19th century, when certain trifling discrepancies were noticed, and with illuminating analogies and examples takes you through the brilliant concepts of Planck, Einstein, Pauli, de Broglie, Bohr, Schroedinger, Heisenberg, Dirac, Sommerfeld, Feynman, etc. This edition includes a new, long postscript carrying the story through 1958. "Of the books attempting an account of the history and contents of our modern atomic physics which have come to my attention, this is the best," H. Margenau, Yale University, in "American Journal of Physics." 32 tables and line illustrations. Index. 275pp. 5⅜ x 8. T518 Paperbound **$1.45**

SPACE AND TIME, Emile Borel. An entirely non-technical introduction to relativity, by world-renowned mathematician, Sorbonne Professor. (Notes on basic mathematics are included separately.) This book has never been surpassed for insight, and extraordinary clarity of thought, as it presents scores of examples, analogies, arguments, illustrations, which explain such topics as: difficulties due to motion; gravitation a force of inertia; geodesic lines; wave-length and difference of phase; x-rays and crystal structure; the special theory of relativity; and much more. Indexes. 4 appendixes. 15 figures. xvi + 243pp. 5⅜ x 8. T592 Paperbound **$1.45**

THE RESTLESS UNIVERSE, Max Born. New enlarged version of this remarkably readable account by a Nobel laureate. Moving from sub-atomic particles to universe, the author explains in very simple terms the latest theories of wave mechanics. Partial contents: air and its relatives, electrons & ions, waves & particles, electronic structure of the atom, nuclear physics. Nearly 1000 illustrations, including 7 animated sequences. 325pp. 6 x 9. T412 Paperbound **$2.00**

SOAP SUBBLES, THEIR COLOURS AND THE FORCES WHICH MOULD THEM, C. V. Boys. Only complete edition, half again as much material as any other. Includes Boys' hints on performing his experiments, sources of supply. Dozens of lucid experiments show complexities of liquid films, surface tension, etc. Best treatment ever written. Introduction. 83 illustrations. Color plate. 202pp. 5⅜ x 8. T542 Paperbound **95¢**

SPINNING TOPS AND GYROSCOPIC MOTION, John Perry. Well-known classic of science still unsurpassed for lucid, accurate, delightful exposition. How quasi-rigidity is induced in flexible and fluid bodies by rapid motions; why gyrostat falls, top rises; nature and effect on climatic conditions of earth's precessional movement; effect of internal fluidity on rotating bodies, etc. Appendixes describe practical uses to which gyroscopes have been put in ships, compasses, monorail transportation. 62 figures. 128pp. 5⅜ x 8. T416 Paperbound **$1.00**

MATTER & LIGHT, THE NEW PHYSICS, L. de Broglie. Non-technical papers by a Nobel laureate explain electromagnetic theory, relativity, matter, light and radiation, wave mechanics, quantum physics, philosophy of science. Einstein, Planck, Bohr, others explained so easily that no mathematical training is needed for all but 2 of the 21 chapters. Unabridged. Index. 300pp. 5⅜ x 8. T35 Paperbound **$1.60**

A SURVEY OF PHYSICAL THEORY, Max Planck. One of the greatest scientists of all time, creator of the quantum revolution in physics, writes in non-technical terms of his own discoveries and those of other outstanding creators of modern physics. Planck wrote this book when science had just crossed the threshold of the new physics, and he communicates the excitement felt then as he discusses electromagnetic theories, statistical methods, evolution of the concept of light, a step-by-step description of how he developed his own momentous theory, and many more of the basic ideas behind modern physics. Formerly "A" Survey of Physics." Bibliography. Index. 128pp. 5⅜ x 8. S650 Paperbound **$1.15**

THE NATURE OF LIGHT AND COLOUR IN THE OPEN AIR, M. Minnaert. Why is falling snow sometimes black? What causes mirages, the fata morgana, multiple suns and moons in the sky? How are shadows formed? Prof. Minnaert of the University of Utrecht answers these and similar questions in optics, light, colour, for non-specialists. Particularly valuable to nature, science students, painters, photographers. Translated by H. M. Kremer-Priest, K. Jay. 202 illustrations, including 42 photos. xvi + 362pp. 5⅜ x 8. T196 Paperbound **$1.95**

THE STORY OF X-RAYS FROM RONTGEN TO ISOTOPES, A. R. Bleich. Non-technical history of x-rays, their scientific explanation, their applications in medicine, industry, research, and art, and their effect on the individual and his descendants. Includes amusing early reactions to Röntgen's discovery, cancer therapy, detections of art and stamp forgeries, potential risks to patient and operator, etc. Illustrations show x-rays of flower structure, the gall bladder, gears with hidden defects, etc. Original Dover publication. Glossary. Bibliography. Index. 55 photos and figures. xiv + 186pp. 5⅜ x 8. T662 Paperbound **$1.35**

TEACH YOURSELF ELECTRICITY, C. W. Wilman. Electrical resistance, inductance, capacitance, magnets, chemical effects of current, alternating currents, generators and motors, transformers, rectifiers, much more. 230 questions, answers, worked examples. List of units. 115 illus. 194pp. 6⅞ x 4¼. Clothbound **$2.00**

TEACH YOURSELF HEAT ENGINES, E. De Ville. Measurement of heat, development of steam and internal combustion engines, efficiency of an engine, compression-ignition engines, production of steam, the ideal engine, much more. 318 exercises, answers, worked examples. Tables. 76 illus. 220pp. 6⅞ x 4¼. Clothbound **$2.00**

TEACH YOURSELF MECHANICS, P. Abbott. The lever, centre of gravity, parallelogram of force, friction, acceleration, Newton's laws of motion, machines, specific gravity, gas, liquid pressure, much more. 280 problems, solutions. Tables. 163 illus. 271pp. 6⅞ x 4¼. Clothbound **$2.00**

GREAT IDEAS OF MODERN MATHEMATICS: THEIR NATURE AND USE, Jagjit Singh. Reader with only high school math will understand main mathematical ideas of modern physics, astronomy, genetics, psychology, evolution, etc., better than many who use them as tools, but comprehend little of their basic structure. Author uses his wide knowledge of non-mathematical fields in brilliant exposition of differential equations, matrices, group theory, logic, statistics, problems of mathematical foundations, imaginary numbers, vectors, etc. Original publication. 2 appendixes. 2 indexes. 65 illustr. 322pp. 5⅜ x 8. S587 Paperbound **$1.55**

MATHEMATICS IN ACTION, O. G. Sutton. Everyone with a command of high school algebra will find this book one of the finest possible introductions to the application of mathematics to physical theory. Ballistics, numerical analysis, waves and wavelike phenomena, Fourier series, group concepts, fluid flow and aerodynamics, statistical measures, and meteorology are discussed with unusual clarity. Some calculus and differential equations theory is developed by the author for the reader's help in the more difficult sections. 88 figures. Index. viii + 236pp. 5⅜ x 8. T440 Clothbound **$3.50**

FREE! All you do is ask for it!

A DOVER SCIENCE SAMPLER, edited by George Barkin. 64-page book, sturdily bound, containing excerpts from over 20 Dover books explaining science. Edwin Hubble, George Sarton, Ernst Mach, A. d'Abro, Galileo, Newton, others, discussing island universes, scientific truth, biological phenomena, stability in bridges, etc. Copies limited, no more than 1 to a customer. FREE

THE FOURTH DIMENSION SIMPLY EXPLAINED, edited by H. P. Manning. 22 essays, originally Scientific American contest entries, that use a minimum of mathematics to explain aspects of 4-dimensional geometry: analogues to 3-dimensional space, 4-dimensional absurdities and curiosities (such as removing the contents of an egg without puncturing its shell), possible measurements and forms, etc. Introduction by the editor. Only book of its sort on a truly elementary level, excellent introduction to advanced works. 82 figures. 251pp. 5⅜ x 8. T711 Paperbound **$1.35**

FAMOUS BRIDGES OF THE WORLD, D. B. Steinman. An up-to-the-minute revised edition of a book that explains the fascinating drama of how the world's great bridges came to be built. The author, designer of the famed Mackinac bridge, discusses bridges from all periods and all parts of the world, explaining their various types of construction, and describing the problems their builders faced. Although primarily for youngsters, this cannot fail to interest readers of all ages. 48 illustrations in the text. 23 photographs. 99pp. 6⅛ x 9¼. T161 Paperbound **$1.00**

BRIDGES AND THEIR BUILDERS, David Steinman and Sara Ruth Watson. Engineers, historians, everyone who has ever been fascinated by great spans will find this book an endless source of information and interest. Dr. Steinman, recipient of the Louis Levy medal, was one of the great bridge architects and engineers of all time, and his analysis of the great bridges of history is both authoritative and easily followed. Greek and Roman bridges, medieval bridges, Oriental bridges, modern works such as the Brooklyn Bridge and the Golden Gate Bridge, and many others are described in terms of history, constructional principles, artistry, and function. All in all this book is the most comprehensive and accurate semipopular history of bridges in print in English. New, greatly revised, enlarged edition. 23 photographs, 26 line drawings. Index. xvii + 401pp. 5⅜ x 8.   T431 Paperbound **$2.00**

FADS AND FALLACIES IN THE NAME OF SCIENCE, Martin Gardner. Examines various cults, quack systems, frauds, delusions which at various times have masqueraded as science. Accounts of hollow-earth fanatics like Symmes; Velikovsky and wandering planets; Hoerbiger; Bellamy and the theory of multiple moons; Charles Fort; dowsing, pseudoscientific methods for finding water, ores, oil. Sections on naturopathy, iridiagnosis, zone therapy, food fads, etc. Analytical accounts of Wilhelm Reich and orgone sex energy; L. Ron Hubbard and Dianetics; A. Korzybski and General Semantics; many others. Brought up to date to include Bridey Murphy, others. Not just a collection of anecdotes, but a fair, reasoned appraisal of eccentric theory. Formerly titled IN THE NAME OF SCIENCE. Preface. Index. x + 384pp. 5⅜ x 8.   T394 Paperbound **$1.50**

See also: A PHILOSOPHICAL ESSAY ON PROBABILITIES, P. de Laplace; ON MATHEMATICS AND MATHEMATICIANS, R. E. Moritz; AN ELEMENTARY SURVEY OF CELESTIAL MECHANICS, Y. Ryabov; THE SKY AND ITS MYSTERIES, E. A. Beet; THE REALM OF THE NEBULAE, E. Hubble; OUT OF THE SKY, H. H. Nininger; SATELLITES AND SCIENTIFIC RESEARCH, D. King-Hele; HEREDITY AND YOUR LIFE, A. M. Winchester; INSECTS AND INSECT LIFE, S. W. Frost; PRINCIPLES OF STRATIGRAPHY, A. W. Grabau; TEACH YOURSELF SERIES.

HISTORY OF SCIENCE AND MATHEMATICS

DIALOGUES CONCERNING TWO NEW SCIENCES, Galileo Galilei. This classic of experimental science, mechanics, engineering, is as enjoyable as it is important. A great historical document giving insights into one of the world's most original thinkers, it is based on 30 years' experimentation. It offers a lively exposition of dynamics, elasticity, sound, ballistics, strength of materials, the scientific method. "Superior to everything else of mine," Galileo. Trans. by H. Crew, A. Salvio. 126 diagrams. Index. xxi + 288pp. 5⅜ x 8.
S99 Paperbound **$1.65**

A DIDEROT PICTORIAL ENCYCLOPEDIA OF TRADES AND INDUSTRY, Manufacturing and the Technical Arts in Plates Selected from "L'Encyclopédie ou Dictionnaire Raisonné des Sciences, des Arts, et des Métiers" of Denis Diderot. Edited with text by C. Gillispie. This first modern selection of plates from the high point of 18th century French engraving is a storehouse of valuable technological information to the historian of arts and science. Over 2000 illustrations on 485 full page plates, most of them original size, show the trades and industries of a fascinating era in such great detail that the processes and shops might very well be reconstructed from them. The plates teem with life, with men, women, and children performing all of the thousands of operations necessary to the trades before and during the early stages of the industrial revolution. Plates are in sequence, and show general operations, closeups of difficult operations, and details of complex machinery. Such important and interesting trades and industries are illustrated as sowing, harvesting, beekeeping, cheesemaking, operating windmills, milling flour, charcoal burning, tobacco processing, indigo, fishing, arts of war, salt extraction, mining, smelting, casting iron, steel, extracting mercury, zinc, sulphur, copper, etc., slating, tinning, silverplating, gilding, making gunpowder, cannons, bells, shoeing horses, tanning, papermaking, printing, dyeing, and more than 40 other categories. Professor Gillispie, of Princeton, supplies a full commentary on all the plates, identifying operations, tools, processes, etc. This material, presented in a lively and lucid fashion, is of great interest to the reader interested in history of science and technology. Heavy library cloth. 920pp. 9 x 12.   T421 Two volume set **$18.50**

DE MAGNETE, William Gilbert. This classic work on magnetism founded a new science. Gilbert was the first to use the word "electricity", to recognize mass as distinct from weight, to discover the effect of heat on magnetic bodies; invent an electroscope, differentiate between static electricity and magnetism, conceive of the earth as a magnet. Written by the first great experimental scientist, this lively work is valuable not only as an historical landmark, but as the delightfully easy to follow record of a perpetually searching, ingenious mind. Translated by P. F. Mottelay. 25 page biographical memoir. 90 figures. lix + 368pp. 5⅜ x 8.   S470 Paperbound **$2.00**

CHARLES BABBAGE AND HIS CALCULATING ENGINES, edited by P. Morrison and E. Morrison. Babbage, leading 19th century pioneer in mathematical machines and herald of modern operational research, was the true father of Harvard's relay computer Mark I. His Difference Engine and Analytical Engine were the first machines in the field. This volume contains a valuable introduction on his life and work; major excerpts from his autobiography, revealing his eccentric and unusual personality; and extensive selections from "Babbage's Calculating Engines," a compilation of hard-to-find journal articles by Babbage, the Countess of Lovelace, L. F. Menabrea, and Dionysius Lardner. 8 illustrations, Appendix of miscellaneous papers. Index. Bibliography. xxxviii + 400pp. 5⅜ x 8.   T12 Paperbound **$2.00**

A HISTORY OF ASTRONOMY FROM THALES TO KEPLER, J. L. E. Dreyer. (Formerly A HISTORY OF PLANETARY SYSTEMS FROM THALES TO KEPLER.) This is the only work in English to give the complete history of man's cosmological views from prehistoric times to Kepler and Newton. Partial contents: Near Eastern astronomical systems, Early Greeks, Homocentric Spheres of Eudoxus, Epicycles, Ptolemaic system, medieval cosmology, Copernicus, Kepler, etc. Revised, foreword by W. H. Stahl. New bibliography. xvii + 430pp. 5⅜ x 8.
S79 Paperbound **$1.98**

A SHORT HISTORY OF ANATOMY AND PHYSIOLOGY FROM THE GREEKS TO HARVEY, Charles Singer. Corrected edition of THE EVOLUTION OF ANATOMY, classic work tracing evolution of anatomy and physiology from prescientific times through Greek & Roman periods, Dark Ages, Renaissance, to age of Harvey and beginning of modern concepts. Centered on individuals, movements, periods that definitely advanced anatomical knowledge: Plato, Diocles, Aristotle, Theophrastus, Herophilus, Erasistratus, the Alexandrians, Galen, Mondino, da Vinci, Linacre, Sylvius, others. Special section on Vesalius; Vesalian atlas of nudes, skeletons, muscle tabulae. Index of names, 20 plates. 270 extremely interesting illustrations of ancient, medieval, Renaissance, Oriental origin. xii + 209pp. 5⅜ x 8.   T389 Paperbound **$1.75**

FROM MAGIC TO SCIENCE, Charles Singer. A great historian examines aspects of medical science from the Roman Empire through the Renaissance. Includes perhaps the best discussion of early herbals, and a penetrating physiological interpretation of "The Visions of Hildegarde of Bingen." Also examined are Arabian and Galenic influences; the Sphere of Pythagoras; Paracelsus; the reawakening of science under Leonardo da Vinci, Vesalius; the Lorica of Gildas the Briton; etc. Frequent quotations with translations. New Introduction by the author. New unabridged, corrected edition. 158 unusual illustrations from classical and medieval sources. Index. xxvii + 365pp. 5⅜ x 8.   T390 Paperbound **$2.00**

HISTORY OF MATHEMATICS, D. E. Smith. Most comprehensive non-technical history of math in English. Discusses lives and works of over a thousand major and minor figures, with footnotes supplying technical information outside the book's scheme, and indicating disputed matters. Vol I: A chronological examination, from primitive concepts through Egypt, Babylonia, Greece, the Orient, Rome, the Middle Ages, the Renaissance, and up to 1900. Vol 2: The development of ideas in specific fields and problems, up through elementary calculus. Two volumes, total of 510 illustrations, 1355pp. 5⅜ x 8. Set boxed in attractive container.   T429, 430 Paperbound, the set **$5.00**

A SHORT ACCOUNT OF THE HISTORY OF MATHEMATICS, W. W. R. Ball. Most readable non-technical history of mathematics treats lives, discoveries of every important figure from Egyptian, Phoenician mathematicians to late 19th century. Discusses schools of Ionia, Pythagoras, Athens, Cyzicus, Alexandria, Byzantium, systems of numeration; primitive arithmetic; Middle Ages, Renaissance, including Arabs, Bacon, Regiomontanus, Tartaglia, Cardan, Stevinus, Galileo, Kepler; modern mathematics of Descartes, Pascal, Wallis, Huygens, Newton, Leibnitz, d'Alembert, Euler, Lambert, Laplace, Legendre, Gauss, Hermite, Weierstrass, scores more. Index. 25 figures. 546pp. 5⅜ x 8.   S630 Paperbound **$2.00**

A SOURCE BOOK IN MATHEMATICS, D. E. Smith. Great discoveries in math, from Renaissance to end of 19th century, in English translation. Read announcements by Dedekind, Gauss, Delamain, Pascal, Fermat, Newton, Abel, Lobachevsky, Bolyai, Riemann, De Moivre, Legendre, Laplace, others of discoveries about imaginary numbers, number congruence, slide rule, equations, symbolism, cubic algebraic equations, non-Euclidean forms of geometry, calculus, function theory, quaternions, etc. Succinct selections from 125 different treatises, articles, most unavailable elsewhere in English. Each article preceded by biographical, historical introduction. Vol. I: Fields of Number, Algebra. Index. 32 illus. 338pp. 5⅜ x 8. Vol. II: Fields of Geometry, Probability, Calculus, Functions, Quaternions. 83 illus. 432pp. 5⅜ x 8.
Vol. 1: S552 Paperbound **$1.85**
Vol. 2: S553 Paperbound **$1.85**
2 vol. set, boxed **$3.50**

A HISTORY OF THE CALCULUS, AND ITS CONCEPTUAL DEVELOPMENT, Carl B. Boyer. Provides laymen and mathematicians a detailed history of the development of the calculus, from early beginning in antiquity to final elaboration as mathematical abstractions. Gives a sense of mathematics not as a technique, but as a habit of mind, in the progression of ideas of Zeno, Plato, Pythagoras, Eudoxus, Arabic and Scholastic mathematicians, Newton, Leibnitz, Taylor, Descartes, Euler, Lagrange, Cantor, Weierstrass, and others. This first comprehensive critical history of the calculus was originally titled "The Concepts of the Calculus." Foreword by R. Courant. Preface. 22 figures. 25-page bibliography. Index. v + 364pp. 5⅜ x 8.   S509 Paperbound **$2.00**

A CONCISE HISTORY OF MATHEMATICS, D. Struik. Lucid study of development of mathematical ideas, techniques from Ancient Near East, Greece, Islamic science, Middle Ages, Renaissance, modern times. Important mathematicians are described in detail. Treatment is not anecdotal, but analytical development of ideas. "Rich in content, thoughtful in interpretation," U.S. QUARTERLY BOOKLIST. Non-technical; no mathematical training needed. Index. 60 illustrations, including Egyptian papyri, Greek mss., portraits of 31 eminent mathematicians. Bibliography. 2nd edition. xix + 299pp. 5⅜ x 8.   T255 Paperbound **$1.75**

See also: **NON-EUCLIDEAN GEOMETRY, R. Bonola; THEORY OF DETERMINANTS IN HISTORICAL ORDER OF DEVELOPMENT, T. Muir; HISTORY OF THE THEORY OF ELASTICITY AND STRENGTH OF MATERIALS, I. Todhunter and K. Pearson; A SHORT HISTORY OF ASTRONOMY, A. Berry; CLASSICS OF SCIENCE.**

PHILOSOPHY OF SCIENCE AND MATHEMATICS

FOUNDATIONS OF SCIENCE: THE PHILOSOPHY OF THEORY AND EXPERIMENT, N. R. Campbell. A critique of the most fundamental concepts of science in general and physics in particular. Examines why certain propositions are accepted without question, demarcates science from philosophy, clarifies the understanding of the tools of science. Part One analyzes the presuppositions of scientific thought: existence of the material world, nature of scientific laws, multiplication of probabilities, etc.; Part Two covers the nature of experiment and the application of mathematics: conditions for measurement, relations between numerical laws and theories, laws of error, etc. An appendix covers problems arising from relativity, force, motion, space, and time. A classic in its field. Index. xiii + 565pp. 5⅝ x 8⅜.
S372 Paperbound **$2.95**

WHAT IS SCIENCE?, Norman Campbell. This excellent introduction explains scientific method, role of mathematics, types of scientific laws. Contents: 2 aspects of science, science & nature, laws of science, discovery of laws, explanation of laws, measurement & numerical laws, applications of science. 192pp. 5⅜ x 8.   S43 Paperbound **$1.25**

THE VALUE OF SCIENCE, Henri Poincaré. Many of the most mature ideas of the "last scientific universalist" covered with charm and vigor for both the beginning student and the advanced worker. Discusses the nature of scientific truth, whether order is innate in the universe or imposed upon it by man, logical thought versus intuition (relating to math, through the works of Weierstrass, Lie, Klein, Riemann), time and space (relativity, psychological time, simultaneity), Hertz's concept of force, interrelationship of mathematical physics to pure math, values within disciplines of Maxwell, Carnot, Mayer, Newton, Lorentz, etc. Index. iii + 147pp. 5⅜ x 8.   S469 Paperbound **$1.35**

SCIENCE AND METHOD, Henri Poincaré. Procedure of scientific discovery, methodology, experiment, idea-germination—the intellectual processes by which discoveries come into being. Most significant and most interesting aspects of development, application of ideas. Chapters cover selection of facts, chance, mathematical reasoning, mathematics, and logic; Whitehead, Russell, Cantor; the new mechanics, etc. 288pp. 5⅜ x 8.   S222 Paperbound **$1.35**

SCIENCE AND HYPOTHESIS, Henri Poincaré. Creative psychology in science. How such concepts as number, magnitude, space, force, classical mechanics were developed, and how the modern scientist uses them in his thought. Hypothesis in physics, theories of modern physics. Introduction by Sir James Larmor. "Few mathematicians have had the breadth of vision of Poincaré, and none is his superior in the gift of clear exposition," E. T. Bell. Index. 272pp. 5⅜ x 8.   S221 Paperbound **$1.35**

PHILOSOPHY AND THE PHYSICISTS, L. S. Stebbing. The philosophical aspects of modern science examined in terms of a lively critical attack on the ideas of Jeans and Eddington. Discusses the task of science, causality, determinism, probability, consciousness, the relation of the world of physics to that of everyday experience. Probes the philosophical significance of the Planck-Bohr concept of discontinuous energy levels, the inferences to be drawn from Heisenberg's Uncertainty Principle, the implications of "becoming" involved in the 2nd law of thermodynamics, and other problems posed by the discarding of Laplacean determinism. 285pp. 5⅜ x 8.   T480 Paperbound **$1.65**

EXPERIMENT AND THEORY IN PHYSICS, Max Born. A Nobel laureate examines the nature and value of the counterclaims of experiment and theory in physics. Synthetic versus analytical scientific advances are analyzed in the work of Einstein, Bohr, Heisenberg, Planck, Eddington, Milne, and others by a fellow participant. 44pp. 5⅜ x 8.   S308 Paperbound **60¢**

THE NATURE OF PHYSICAL THEORY, P. W. Bridgman. Here is how modern physics looks to a highly unorthodox physicist—a Nobel laureate. Pointing out many absurdities of science, and demonstrating the inadequacies of various physical theories, Dr. Bridgman weighs and analyzes the contributions of Einstein, Bohr, Newton, Heisenberg, and many others. This is a non-technical consideration of the correlation of science and reality. Index. xi + 138pp. 5⅜ x 8.   S33 Paperbound **$1.25**

THE PHILOSOPHY OF SPACE AND TIME, H. Reichenbach. An important landmark in the development of the empiricist conception of geometry, covering the problem of the foundations of geometry, the theory of time, the consequences of Einstein's relativity, including: relations between theory and observations; coordinate and metrical properties of space; the psychological problem of visual intuition of non-Euclidean structures; and many other important topics in modern science and philosophy. The majority of ideas require only a knowledge of intermediate math. Introduction by R. Carnap. 49 figures. Index. xviii + 296pp. 5⅜ x 8.
S443 Paperbound **$2.00**

MATTER & MOTION, James Clerk Maxwell, This excellent exposition begins with simple particles and proceeds gradually to physical systems beyond complete analysis: motion, force, properties of centre of mass of material system, work, energy, gravitation, etc. Written with all Maxwell's original insights and clarity. Notes by E. Larmor. 17 diagrams. 178pp. 5⅜ x 8.
S188 Paperbound **$1.35**

THE ANALYSIS OF MATTER, Bertrand Russell. How do our senses concord with the new physics? This volume covers such topics as logical analysis of physics, prerelativity physics, causality, scientific inference, physics and perception, special and general relativity, Weyl's theory, tensors, invariants and their physical interpretation, periodicity and qualitative series. "The most thorough treatment of the subject that has yet been published," THE NATION. Introduction by L. E. Denonn. 422pp. 5⅜ x 8.   T231 Paperbound **$1.95**

SUBSTANCE AND FUNCTION, & EINSTEIN'S THEORY OF RELATIVITY, Ernst Cassirer. Two books bound as one. Cassirer establishes a philosophy of the exact sciences that takes into consideration newer developments in mathematics, and also shows historical connections. Partial contents: Aristotelian logic, Mill's analysis, Helmholtz & Kronecker, Russell & cardinal numbers, Euclidean vs. non-Euclidean geometry, Einstein's relativity. Bibliography. Index. xxi + 465pp. 5⅜ x 8.   T50 Paperbound **$2.00**

PRINCIPLES OF MECHANICS, Heinrich Hertz. This last work by the great 19th century physicist is not only a classic, but of great interest in the logic of science. Creating a new system of mechanics based upon space, time, and mass, it returns to axiomatic analysis, to understanding of the formal or structural aspects of science, taking into account logic, observation, and a priori elements. Of great historical importance to Poincaré, Carnap, Einstein, Milne. A 20-page introduction by R. S. Cohen, Wesleyan University, analyzes the implications of Hertz's thought and the logic of science. Bibliography. 13-page introduction by Helmholtz. xlii + 274pp. 5⅜ x 8.   S316 Clothbound **$3.50**
S317 Paperbound **$1.85**

THE PHILOSOPHICAL WRITINGS OF PEIRCE, edited by Justus Buchler. (Formerly published as THE PHILOSOPHY OF PEIRCE.) This is a carefully balanced exposition of Peirce's complete system, written by Peirce himself. It covers such matters as scientific method, pure chance vs. law, symbolic logic, theory of signs, pragmatism, experiment, and other topics. Introduction by Justus Buchler, Columbia University. xvi + 368pp. 5⅜ x 8.
T217 Paperbound **$1.95**

ESSAYS IN EXPERIMENTAL LOGIC, John Dewey. This stimulating series of essays touches upon the relationship between inquiry and experience, dependence of knowledge upon thought, character of logic; judgments of practice, data and meanings, stimuli of thought, etc. Index. viii + 444pp. 5⅜ x 8.   T73 Paperbound **$1.95**

LANGUAGE, TRUTH AND LOGIC, A. Ayer. A clear introduction to the Vienna and Cambridge schools of Logical Positivism. It sets up specific tests by which you can evaluate validity of ideas, etc. Contents: Function of philosophy, elimination of metaphysics, nature of analysis, a priori, truth and probability, etc. 10th printing. "I should like to have written it myself," Bertrand Russell. Index. 160pp. 5⅜ x 8.   T10 Paperbound **$1.25**

THE PSYCHOLOGY OF INVENTION IN THE MATHEMATICAL FIELD, J. Hadamard. Where do ideas come from? What role does the unconscious play? Are ideas best developed by mathematical reasoning, word reasoning, visualization? What are the methods used by Einstein, Poincaré, Galton, Riemann? How can these techniques be applied by others? Hadamard, one of the world's leading mathematicians, discusses these and other questions. xiii + 145pp. 5⅜ x 8.
T107 Paperbound **$1.25**

FOUNDATIONS OF GEOMETRY, Bertrand Russell. Analyzing basic problems in the overlap area between mathematics and philosophy, Nobel laureate Russell examines the nature of geometrical knowledge, the nature of geometry, and the application of geometry to space. It covers the history of non-Euclidean geometry, philosophic interpretations of geometry—especially Kant—projective and metrical geometry. This is most interesting as the solution offered in 1897 by a great mind to a problem still current. New introduction by Prof. Morris Kline of N. Y. University. xii + 201pp. 5⅜ x 8.   S232 Clothbound **$3.25**
S233 Paperbound **$1.60**

TEACH YOURSELF books. For adult self-study, for refresher and supplementary study.

The most effective series of home study mathematics books on the market! With absolutely no outside help, they will teach you as much as any similar college or high-school course, or will helpfully supplement any such course. Each step leads directly to the next, each question is anticipated. Numerous lucid examples and carefully-wrought practice problems illustrate meanings. Not skimpy outlines, not surveys, not usual classroom texts, these 204- to 380-page books are packed with the finest instruction you'll find anywhere for adult self-study.

TEACH YOURSELF ALGEBRA, P. Abbott. Formulas, coordinates, factors, graphs of quadratic functions, quadratic equations, logarithms, ratio, irrational numbers, arithmetical, geometrical series, much more. 1241 problems, solutions. Tables. 52 illus. 307pp. 6⅞ x 4¼.
Clothbound **$2.00**

TEACH YOURSELF GEOMETRY, P. Abbott. Solids, lines, points, surfaces, angle measurement, triangles, theorem of Pythagoras, polygons, loci, the circle, tangents, symmetry, solid geometry, prisms, pyramids, solids of revolution, etc. 343 problems, solutions. 268 illus. 334pp. 6⅞ x 4¼.
Clothbound **$2.00**

TEACH YOURSELF TRIGONOMETRY, P. Abbott. Geometrical foundations, indices, logarithms, trigonometrical ratios, relations between sides, angles of triangle, circular measure, trig. ratios of angles of any magnitude, much more. Requires elementary algebra, geometry. 465 problems, solutions. Tables. 102 illus. 204pp. 6⅞ x 4¼.
Clothbound **$2.00**

TEACH YOURSELF THE CALCULUS, P. Abbott. Variations in functions, differentiation, solids of revolution, series, elementary differential equations, areas by integral calculus, much more. Requires algebra, trigonometry. 970 problems, solutions. Tables. 89 illus. 380pp. 6⅞ x 4¼.
Clothbound **$2.00**

TEACH YOURSELF THE SLIDE RULE, B. Snodgrass. Fractions, decimals, A-D scales, log-log scales, trigonometrical scales, indices, logarithms. Commercial, precision, electrical, dualistic, Brighton rules. 80 problems, solutions. 10 illus. 207pp. 6⅞ x 4¼. Clothbound **$2.00**

See also: **TEACH YOURSELF ELECTRICITY, C. W. Wilman; TEACH YOURSELF HEAT ENGINES, E. De Ville; TEACH YOURSELF MECHANICS, P. Abbott.**

✳   ✳   ✳

HOW DO YOU USE A SLIDE RULE? by A. A. Merrill. Not a manual for mathematicians and engineers, but a lucid step-by-step explanation that presents the fundamental rules clearly enough to be understood by anyone who could benefit by the use of a slide rule in his work or business. This work concentrates on the 2 most important operations: multiplication and division. 10 easy lessons, each with a clear drawing, will save you countless hours in your banking, business, statistical, and other work. First publication. Index. 2 Appendixes. 10 illustrations. 78 problems, all with answers. vi + 36pp. 6⅛ x 9¼. T62 Paperbound **60¢**

THEORY OF OPERATION OF THE SLIDE RULE, J. P. Ellis. Not a skimpy "instruction manual", but an exhaustive treatment that will save you uncounted hours throughout your career. Supplies full understanding of every scale on the Log Log Duplex Decitrig type of slide rule. Shows the most time-saving methods, and provides practice useful in the widest variety of actual engineering situations. Each operation introduced in terms of underlying logarithmic theory. Summary of prerequisite math. First publication. Index. 198 figures. Over 450 problems with answers. Bibliography. 12 Appendices. ix + 289pp. 5⅜ x 8.
S727 Paperbound **$1.50**

ARITHMETICAL EXCURSIONS: AN ENRICHMENT OF ELEMENTARY MATHEMATICS, H. Bowers and J. Bowers. For students who want unusual methods of arithmetic never taught in school; for adults who want to increase their number sense. Little known facts about the most simple numbers, arithmetical entertainments and puzzles, figurate numbers, number chains, mysteries and folklore of numbers, the "Hin-dog-abic" number system, etc. First publication. Index. 529 numbered problems and diversions, all with answers. Bibliography. 50 figures. xiv + 320pp. 5⅜ x 8.
T770 Paperbound **$1.65**

APPLIED MATHEMATICS FOR RADIO AND COMMUNICATIONS ENGINEERS, C. E. Smith. No extraneous material here!—only the theories, equations, and operations essential and immediately useful for radio work. Can be used as refresher, as handbook of applications and tables, or as full home-study course. Ranges from simplest arithmetic through calculus, series, and wave forms, hyperbolic trigonometry, simultaneous equations in mesh circuits, etc. Supplies applications right along with each math topic discussed. 22 useful tables of functions, formulas, logs, etc. Index. 166 exercises, 140 examples, all with answers. 95 diagrams. Bibliography. x + 336pp. 5⅜ x 8.
S141 Paperbound **$1.75**

BIBLIOGRAPHIES

GUIDE TO THE LITERATURE OF MATHEMATICS AND PHYSICS, N. G. Parke III. Over 5000 entries included under approximately 120 major subject headings, of selected most important books, monographs, periodicals, articles in English, plus important works in German, French, Italian, Spanish, Russian (many recently available works). Covers every branch of physics, math, related engineering. Includes author, title, edition, publisher, place, date, number of volumes, number of pages. A 40-page introduction on the basic problems of research and study provides useful information on the organization and use of libraries, the psychology of learning, etc. This reference work will save you hours of time. 2nd revised edition. Indices of authors, subjects. 464pp. 5⅜ x 8.   S447 Paperbound **$2.49**

THE STUDY OF THE HISTORY OF MATHEMATICS & THE STUDY OF THE HISTORY OF SCIENCE, George Sarton. Scientific method & philosophy in 2 scholarly fields. Defines duty of historian of math., provides especially useful bibliography with best available biographies of modern mathematicians, editions of their collected works, correspondence. Observes combination of history & science, will aid scholar in understanding science today. Bibliography includes best known treatises on historical methods. 200-item critically evaluated bibliography. Index. 10 illustrations. 2 volumes bound as one. 113pp. + 75pp. 5⅜ x 8.
T240 Paperbound **$1.25**

MATHEMATICAL PUZZLES

AMUSEMENTS IN MATHEMATICS, Henry Ernest Dudeney. The foremost British originator of mathematical puzzles is always intriguing, witty, and paradoxical in this classic, one of the largest collections of mathematical amusements. More than 430 puzzles, problems, and paradoxes. Mazes and games, problems on number manipulation, unicursal and other route problems, puzzles on measuring, weighing, packing, age, kinship, chessboards, joiners', crossing river, plane figure dissection, and many others. Solutions. More than 450 illustrations. vii + 258pp. 5⅜ x 8.   T473 Paperbound **$1.25**

THE CANTERBURY PUZZLES, Henry Ernest Dudeney. Chaucer's pilgrims set one another problems in story form. Also Adventures of the Puzzle Club, the Strange Escape of the King's Jester, the Monks of Riddlewell, the Squire's Christmas Puzzle Party, and others. All puzzles are original, based on dissecting plane figures, arithmetic, algebra, elementary calculus, and other branches of mathematics, and purely logical ingenuity. "The limit of ingenuity and intricacy . . ." The Observer. Over 110 puzzles. Full solutions. 150 illustrations. viii + 225pp. 5⅜ x 8.   T474 Paperbound **$1.25**

SYMBOLIC LOGIC and THE GAME OF LOGIC, Lewis Carroll. "Symbolic Logic" is not concerned with modern symbolic logic, but is instead a collection of over 380 problems posed with charm and imagination, using the syllogism, and a fascinating diagrammatic method of drawing conclusions. In "The Game of Logic," Carroll's whimsical imagination devises a logical game played with 2 diagrams and counters (included) to manipulate hundreds of tricky syllogisms. The final section, "Hit or Miss" is a lagniappe of 101 additional puzzles in the delightful Carroll manner. Until this reprint edition, both of these books were rarities costing up to $15 each. Symbolic Logic: Index, xxxi + 199pp. The Game of Logic: 96pp. Two vols. bound as one. 5⅜ x 8.   T492 Paperbound **$1.50**

Dover publishes books on art, music, philosophy, literature, languages, history, social sciences, psychology, handcrafts, orientalia, puzzles and entertainments, chess, pets and gardens, books explaining science, intermediate and higher mathematics, mathematical physics, engineering, biological sciences, earth sciences, classics of science, etc. Write to:

> *Dept. catrr.*
> *Dover Publications, Inc.*
> *180 Varick Street, N. Y. 14, N. Y.*

1931